FIBONACCI'S RABBITS

First published in Great Britain, Australia and New Zealand in 2019 by Modern Books
An imprint of Elwin Street Productions Limited
14 Clerkenwell Green
London EC1R 0DP
www.modern-books.com

Additional text by John Farndon
Interior design and illustrations: Jason Anscomb, Rawshock design.
Photo credits: Shutterstock.com, except page 117: public domain

ISBN 978-1-912827-03-9

10 9 8 7 6 5 4 3 2 1

Printed in Slovenia

FIBONACCI'S RABBITS

AND 49 OTHER DISCOVERIES THAT REVOLUTIONISED MATHEMATICS

ADAM HART-DAVIS

(m)

Contents

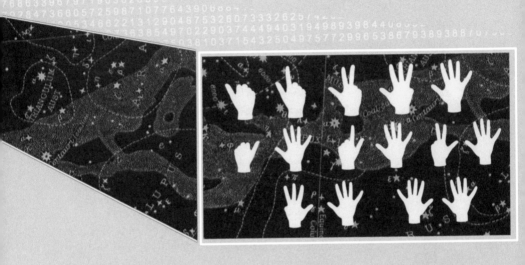

Moving on from simple practical problems to abstract ideas must have been a big step. Much of this early stage is lost, since nothing was written down until the rise of the Greek civilization, which flourished in city states around the Mediterranean, notably Croton, Athens, and Alexandria. One of the earliest of the Greek philosophers, Thales of Miletus, predicted an eclipse of the sun, an event that was so impressive that it is said to have stopped a war. Exactly how Thales made his prediction is unknown, but it is likely that mathematics was involved.

ca **20,000** BCE

ASSOCIATED
MATHEMATICIANS:
Ancient humans

CONCLUSION:
Early humans counted by
making notches on bones

WHAT IS ON THE ISHANGO BONE?

THE EARLIEST EVIDENCE OF COUNTING

The ancient history of life on Earth is written in the fossil record – the remains of ancient life forms that have been preserved, and found or dug out of the rocks. Bones are tougher than soft tissue, and therefore more often preserved.

A few ancient bones may also contain evidence of the dawn of mathematics. These bones had notches carved into them by ancient humans, which indicates various kinds of counting systems were in use many thousands of years ago.

The Lebombo bone

The Lebombo bone was found by archaeologist Peter Beaumont in the 1970s in a cave in the Lebombo Mountains, between South Africa and Swaziland. This 8 centimetre (3.2 inch) long baboon fibula (leg bone) is 44,000 years old, and has exactly 29 notches. It may just have been used as a measuring stick, but the fact that there are 29 notches suggests that it could have been a lunar calendar.

Perhaps the people there held a meeting or a celebration at every new moon, asking for the moon to be reborn. The moon takes about 29 days for each complete cycle, so a bone with 29 notches would allow the owner to predict when the next new moon was due. However, the bone is clearly broken at one end; there may originally have been more than 29 notches.

The Ishango bone

Ishango is part of the Virunga National Park in the Democratic Republic of Congo, home to one of the sources of the Nile. Here, in 1960, a Belgian explorer, Jean de Heinzelin de Braucourt (1920–1998) found a thin brown bone, which turned out also to be the fibula of a baboon. It's 10 centimetres (4 inches) long,

about the size of a pencil, and appears to be a writing or scribing instrument, since it has a piece of quartz fixed to one end. Along its length, however, are a series of organized notches, clearly carved deliberately.

The Ishango bone has been estimated at around 20,000 years old, and has three rows or columns of scratch marks or notches along its length. They are arranged in clear groups, and seem to represent numbers. The top row has 7, 5, 5, 10, 8, 4, 6, and 3 (total 48). The second row has 9, 19, 21, and 11 (total 60). The third row has 19, 17, 13, and 11 (total 60).

Marks on the Ishango bone

Split tally sticks

Originally the bone was thought to be a tally stick. Such sticks are found frequently, and seem to have been used for mnemonic purposes (as memory joggers).

Split tally sticks, often made of hazel, were used in financial transactions. A single series of notches recorded the amount, then the stick was split, so that each half carried all the notches and each party could keep a record of the transaction.

A lunar calendar

Another possibility is that the bone represents a six-month calendar of the phases of the moon. The moon takes about seven days for each quarter-cycle – from full to half, from half to new moon, and so on. The top row might have been someone's attempt to record all the nights in each successive quarter, allowing for the possibility that the Ishango region was cloudy much of the time, making observation difficult.

Evidence of early mathematics?

For 60 years scholars have been arguing about the significance of these numbers. De Heinzelin's original reckoning was that they formed an arithmetical game of some sort. Others have suggested that because the totals of the rows are 60 and 48, both multiples of 12, they might have formed the basis of a duodecimal system – counting in base 12.

Reading from right to left, the top row has three notches, then doubles to six notches, four then doubles to eight, followed by 10, which is halved to five. The second and third rows have only odd numbers of notches. In the second row the number of notches is $(10 - 1)$, $(20 - 1)$, $(20 + 1)$, and $(10 + 1)$. The third row has four groups, each containing a prime number; in fact it has all the prime numbers between 10 and 20. Could people possibly have grasped the concept of prime numbers 20,000 years ago? This seems unlikely. Mathematical historian Peter Rudman has estimated that prime numbers were not understood until about 2,500 years ago, and the concept of division appears to date back only about 10,000 years. Nonetheless, while the meaning of these numbers is unclear, without these first developments in counting, mathematics as we know it would not exist.

WHY DO WE COUNT TO '10'?

THE ORIGIN OF NUMERALS

20,000 – 3400 BCE

ASSOCIATED
MATHEMATICIANS:
Ancient humans

CONCLUSION:
The Hindu-Arabic numerals
we use have won out
over many other
numeral systems.

Counting is finding the number of a set of objects, such as words in a sentence or nuts on a plate, by labelling them. When the objects are separated over time or space – rain showers through the day, or sheep scattered over the moor – then it might be easier to use a tally system, with marks on a piece of paper or notches on a stick.

The Lebombo bone (see previous entry) and other tally sticks suggest that such a counting system was in use 44,000 years ago. People might have counted the number of members in their group, the number of prey animals in a herd, or the number of their enemies.

Counting without speech

Fingers make a good tally system. If there are fewer than 10 nuts on a plate, then you can put one finger beside or on each nut and note how many fingers are in use. This means you do not have to worry about the concept of 'five' or 'seven', or even about the idea of numbers at all. You only have to register that the nuts reached to the middle finger of your left hand.

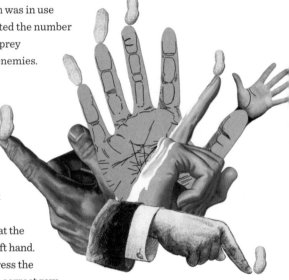

You would not even need speech to express the number of nuts; you could just hold up the correct row of fingers. In many cultures the symbol for a single object is similar to our 'one', which could well be the representation of a single finger held up. If you go into any pub in Dublin today and hold up one finger, you will get a pint of Guinness.

New number systems

We don't know exactly when people began to talk – that is, to use words – but it is likely that soon after they began to use language they would have made up words for numbers, even if counting was of the form 'one', 'two', 'very many'.

In the Zagros Mountains of Iran, clay tokens from over 6,000 years ago have been found that were used as records for numbers of animals. A token with a plus sign stamped on it represented one sheep; two such tokens stood for two sheep. A different token represented 10 sheep; another for 10 goats. These are some of the earliest representations of counting and numbers that aren't denoted by tallying.

The first abstract numerals seem to have been written down around 3100 BCE, by the Sumerians, who lived in Mesopotamia, now part of Iraq. The Sumerians counted in base 60 (see next entry) and had several number systems used for different classes of objects, such as distinct terms for counting animals or measurements, rather as the Japanese do today.

A little later, around 3000 BCE, the Egyptians developed their own written numerals. This system was similar to Roman numerals, with different symbols representing the powers of

10 (1, 10, 100, etc). Most notably, the Egyptian numeral system used fractions, indicated by the 'open mouth' hieroglyph. This new development was likely driven by practical need, such as the problem of dividing food among several people.

Chinese, Roman and Arabic numerals

More than 2,500 years ago, Chinese mathematicians and merchants began to use rods for counting and calculating. Each rod denoted a different value, depending on its position and whether it was horizontal or vertical. When they needed a zero, they just left a blank. Sometimes they used red rods for positive numbers and black rods for negative numbers – or rods with triangular sections for negative numbers.

Roman numerals evolved from a primitive system of carving notches in wood, bone, or stone. The symbols I, II, III, IV, V, VI, VII, VIII, IX, and X stand for 1 to 10; all these numbers are made of straight lines, and so are easy to carve. L for 50 and M for 1,000 are also easy, although C for 100 and D for 500 are trickier. Roman numerals are hopeless for calculation: try multiplying CMIX by IV, rather than 909 × 4.

In the sixth century CE, the Indians simplified and codified their number system into a decimal-place value system similar to our own. This system evolved out of several earlier systems of numerals, going back to around 3000 BCE. The Arabs incorporated the Indian system, including the use of zero as a placeholder, into their own number system in the ninth century.

These numerals were far more intuitive for calculating. This is largely because of the place-value system, in which numerals denote different values depending on their position in a number. For example, 9 can mean both nine tens in 190 and nine hundreds in 907. The simplicity of this system was a huge improvement on Roman numerals, which were still used in Europe at this time. Fibonacci presented this numeral system to Europeans in Latin in his *Liber Abaci* in 1202 (see page 57), which is why we now have 'Arabic' numerals 1 through 10.

ca 2700 BCE

ASSOCIATED
MATHEMATICIANS:
The Sumerians

CONCLUSION:
Many of the figures
we use today come from
the ancient Sumerian
number system.

WHY ARE THERE SIXTY SECONDS IN A MINUTE?

THE SUMERIAN SEXAGESIMAL SYSTEM

We live in a decimal world, a world of nice round tens, hundreds, thousands, millions. So why, then, are so many of our fundamental units – hours of the day, minutes of an hour, degrees in a circle, and so on – based on numbers divisible by six, such as 12, 60 and 360? Is it just an awkward historical hangover? Or is there more to it than that?

Wedge-shaped numbers

The sexagesimal, or 60-based, system originated four to five thousand years ago in the ancient Sumerian civilization in Mesopotamia. Sumerian mathematics was perhaps the most sophisticated in the ancient world. Maths may have been equally well developed in other civilizations, but we know Sumerians were maths whizzes because they wrote their maths down in stone – or rather, clay tablets.

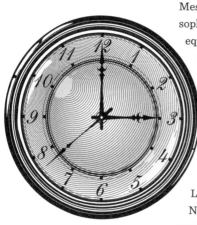

The Sumerians developed one of the earliest writing systems. To record language and maths, they made a wedge-shaped mark in damp clay tablets with a stick called a stylus. The tablets then dried and hardened in the sun to preserve their messages forever. The wedge-shapes give the writing the name *cuneiform*, from the Latin for 'wedge', *cuneus*.

Numbers are shown with a simple combination of downward marks and marks at an angle. A single downward mark is one, a unit, two marks are two, three marks is three and so on. But the layout of downward marks meant that they could mean one, 60 or 3,600. Numbers in between were done as multiples of 60. So 124 would be two 60 marks plus four single-unit marks.

Why 60?

So it's a little like Roman numerals, but the system is based on 60, not ten. But why 60? Mathematicians have been theorizing about why for a long time, and there is no definitive answer. In the fourth century CE, Theon of Alexandria suggested it was because 60 is the smallest number divisible by one, two, three, four and five so the number of divisors is maximized. But there are other numbers with good numbers of divisors.

The Austrian-American science historian Otto Neugebauer argued that it emerged from Sumerian weights and measures, and 60 allowed easy division of goods into thirds, halves, quarters and fifths. Some argue, though, that maybe the number system led to the measure system rather than the other way round.

Then there are those who think it's all in the stars. The night sky was very clear back then, and there wasn't much to do at night. Sumerians were avid stargazers, and looked for patterns in the sky, making up the first constellation names. The stars became their calendar – the star pattern moves on slightly every night, eventually coming back to the same place after a year.

In this way, the Sumerians worked out that the year is 365 days long. Nineteenth-century German mathematician Moritz Cantor decided they rounded it down to 360, leading to their base 60 – by dividing it by six (it's very easy to divide a circle by six). It's certainly plausible, and a 360-day year would conveniently split into 12 thirty-day months, and might explain why we now have 360 degrees in a circle. But this is mere speculation.

Maybe it simply comes from finger counting. However, there's evidence that people in Mesopotamia finger-counted in a rather different way. On one hand, you use your thumb to count the three bits between the joints on each of your four

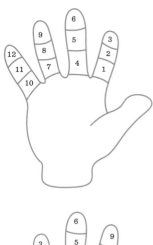

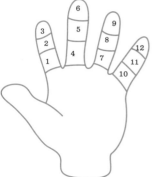

fingers, giving you 12. For each 12, you flick up the thumb on the other hand, then the four fingers, giving five times 12 or 60. It's beautifully simple and very quick once you get the hang of it.

The advantages of calculating in base 60

However it came about, 60 is divisible by so many numbers that it gave the Sumerians the basis for the development of some very sophisticated maths. In 2017, Australian mathematicians led by David Mansfield claimed to have finally cracked the code for the Babylonian tablet known as Plimpton 322. This 3,800-year-old clay tablet was found in Iraq a century ago by a real-life Indiana Jones, Edgar J Banks, and then sold to New York publisher George Plimpton before being bequeathed to Columbia University.

The tablet shows a complex table of figures in the Babylonian version of cuneiform, and Mansfield and his colleagues claim that not only is this an early trigonometric table, but that this table is actually more accurate than modern decimal tables because of the divisibility of numbers using 60 as a base – 60 is divisible by three, and 10 isn't. It's easy to write the fractions 1/2, 1/4, and 1/5 in base 10 – 0.5, 0.25, and 0.2, and so on. But 1/3 is 0.3333, a never-ending decimal, and so never precise.

Whether Mansfield's right is open to debate. But they've certainly highlighted the pluses of 60 as a number base. We are now totally used to the convenience of our 10-based decimal system in which we simply change positions when dividing or multiplying by 10, and decimal fractions have opened the way to an infinite range of calculations. But with practical fractions, such as divisions of time, the divisibility of 60 has its own advantages – advantages so strong that they have persisted through the ages while other systems have come and gone. Few people seriously suggest moving to the 10-hour day and the 10-minute hour. Dividing your time is just so much easier with base 60.

CAN THE CIRCLE BE SQUARED?

HOW THE GREEKS WRESTLED WITH IRRATIONAL NUMBERS

ca 1650 BCE

ASSOCIATED
MATHEMATICIANS:
Ancient Egyptians,
ancient Greeks

CONCLUSION:
Since π is a transcendental
number, squaring the circle
is impossible.

One of the oldest challenges that presented itself to ancient mathematicians was the squaring of the circle. Using ruler and compass only, could they construct a square with the same area as a given circle? Essentially this boils down to finding a precise value for π (pi), the ratio of the circumference of a circle to its diameter. Given a circle with a radius of one unit – it could be 1 mm or 1 km – its area would be πr^2 or π square units. The square of the same area would have to have sides of the square root of π, or approximately 1.772 units.

This problem is tackled in the ancient Egyptian Rhind papyrus (see next entry), where it is used to provide a rough value for the area of a circular field. Here, the rule is to cut 1/9 off the diameter and form a square with sides the length of the remainder, giving a square with a similar area to the circle. This gives an approximation of pi at 256/81 or 3.16049: reasonably close to our modern value of 3.14159. Close, but it does not solve the problem of squaring the circle. The race to square the circle really took off, however, with the Greeks.

Estimating π

The first Greek known to have studied the problem of squaring the circle was Anaxagoras, while he was in prison in Athens in around 440 BCE. A few years later Antiphon drew a square inside a circle, then doubled the sides to make an octagon, then doubled these again to make a 16-sided polygon, and so on, until the area of the polygon, which he could calculate, was almost equal to that of the circle.

Lunes

Hippocrates' method

Meanwhile, Hippocrates of Chios (not to be confused with the doctor, who came from Kos) constructed semicircles on all three sides of an isosceles right-angled triangle, and showed that the sum of the two *lunes* (the crescent-shaped area bounded by two overlapping circles) was equal to the area of the triangle. All he had to do then was construct a square with an area equal to that of the triangle – but he could not work out how to do so.

Is it impossible?

Over the centuries many mathematicians tried to solve the problem, until it seemed impossible. 'Squaring the circle' came to mean attempting the impossible, like holding back the tides.

Lewis Carroll, author of *Alice in Wonderland*, was the pen name of Victorian mathematician Charles Lutwidge Dodgson. He liked to debunk bogus theories of how the circle might be squared, and in his diary of 1855 wrote that he hoped to write a book on 'Plain Facts for Circle-squarers'.

To square the circle you have to construct a line of length $\sqrt{\pi}$. It was shown in 1837 that particular lengths could be constructed if they were whole numbers, or rational numbers such as 3/5, or even some irrational numbers. An irrational number is a number that cannot be written as a fraction involving only integers. Thus 3/5 is rational, and so is 1001/799, but the square root of two is irrational. We can write it as 1.4142135623731, but it is not equal to any whole number divided by another, and the decimal does not repeat itself, unlike 1/7, for example, which is 0.142857142857142857... The square root of two, however, even though it is irrational, can be written as the product of an equation with whole-number coefficients: $x^2 = 2$. That makes it an algebraic number, and it is possible to construct a line with a length of any algebraic number.

Transcendental numbers

Unfortunately, π is not only irrational but also transcendental, which means that it cannot be calculated as the answer to any such equation. In 1882 German mathematician Ferdinand von

Lindemann proved that π is transcendental, and therefore that a line of length π (or its square root) cannot be constructed.

Almost all real numbers are transcendental, although it is incredibly difficult to prove that any given number is transcendental. There are several numbers used in contemporary mathematical research that are not yet proven to be either algebraic or transcendental. In order to prove a number is transcendental, it must be shown not to be the answer to any algebraic equation. Given this defining quality, relatively few of these numbers are used in mathematics, as nearly all of them are exceedingly difficult to work with.

In number theory, Lindemann's findings are often taken with those of his contemporary Karl Weierstrass to form the Lindemann-Weierstrass theorem. The theorem uses complex proofs to give a method for proving that numbers are transcendental. It follows directly from the theorem that both π and e are transcendental and they are by far the most commonly used transcendental numbers.

By proving π was transcendental, the Lindemann-Weierstrass theorem also proved that a line of length $\sqrt{\pi}$ cannot be constructed. This result from nineteenth century number theory thus solved a centuries-old classical geometry problem. They had proven, once and for all, that the circle couldn't be squared.

ca **1500** BCE

**ASSOCIATED
MATHEMATICIANS:**

Ancient Egyptians

CONCLUSION:

A chance find gave
us a profound insight
into ancient Egyptian
mathematics.

WHAT MAKES A
FRACTION EGYPTIAN?

THE RHIND PAPYRUS AND
EGYPTIAN MATHEMATICS

In 1858, young Scots antiquarian Alexander Rhind came
across an ancient Egyptian papyrus scroll in a market in Luxor.
It had probably been dug up illegally, and after Rhind's death
just a few years later it was sold to the British Museum. The
Rhind papyrus, as it is now known, turns out to be one of the
most ancient maths texts, written 3,550 years ago by a scribe
called Ahmose as he copied a more ancient text.

Once you've deciphered it all, it's like a school textbook of
84 maths problems. It's divided into three books. The first one
covers familiar territory, arithmetic and algebra; the second is
about geometry and the last is miscellaneous. Remarkably, the
Rhind papyrus shows that the Egyptian number system was
decimal, making it even more familiar to us.

Egyptian fractions

But in fractions there is a significant difference so intriguing that Egyptian fractions have become a topic of interest in modern number theory. In Egyptian fractions, the numerator is always one (except in the case of 2/3). So if you wanted to express five eighths as a fraction, Egyptians wouldn't write 5/8 but the sum 1/2 + 1/8. Nowadays, any fraction written as a sum of unit fractions is called an Egyptian fraction.

This has real practical advantages. Think of this problem. You have five pizzas to divide between eight people. Conventional fractions tell you that everyone gets 5/8 of a pizza each. But how do you actually cut that? It's a nightmare. With Egyptian fractions however, it couldn't be simpler. As we said, Egyptian fractions express 5/8 as 1/2 + 1/8. At once the answer becomes clear. You divide four of the pizzas in half, and the last one into eighths. So everyone gets 1/2 + 1/8. It's so much simpler it seems like magic.

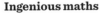

But for number theorists, it doesn't end there. It turns out there are some very interesting things about Egyptian fractions. First, you can express any fraction less than one as an Egyptian fraction. Secondly, you can split any ordinary fraction into an infinite number of Egyptian fractions: 3/4 = 1/2 + 1/8 + 1/12 + 1/48 + 1/72 + 1/144 and so on.

Ingenious maths

The more modern number theorists delve into the Rhind papyrus, the more they realize the ingenuities of Egyptian maths. The Egyptian way of multiplying, for instance, involves repeated doublings which, when set out, bear a remarkable resemblance to binary maths: the maths that underpins computing. And their way of working out the area of a circle, long before Archimedes, was rough and ready, but yielded workable results, using a value of pi within barely half a per cent of our modern value (see previous entry).

All this is not to say that the ancient Egyptians were mathematical geniuses. Rather that it is easy to get trapped by habitual ways of thinking, and different approaches can lead to new insights.

ASSOCIATED
MATHEMATICIAN:

Pythagoras

WHAT IS PROOF?

PYTHAGORAS'S THEOREM

CONCLUSION:

The idea that proofs are
vital in mathematics can be
traced back to Pythagoras
and his famous theorem.

It's got to be the most famous mathematical theorem of all –
Pythagoras's theorem. It's one of the few mathematical theorems
children learn off by heart. 'In a right-angle triangle, the square
of the hypotenuse is equal to the sum of the squares of the other
two sides.' The hypotenuse is the longest side, opposite the right
angle, and comes from the Greek word for stretching.

But it wasn't Pythagoras's idea. If Pythagoras actually
existed – and it is by no means certain he did; 'Pythagoras' may
just have been the name for a group with similar beliefs – then
the idea was already a thousand or more years old by the time
he came on the scene. Clay tablets show the Babylonians knew
it, and there's every chance the ancient Egyptians did too – you
only have to look at the pyramids to see right-angled triangles
in action. The ancient Chinese knew it and it is recorded
in the ancient Indian text the *Shulba Sutra*, dated to
around 600 BCE.

The beginning of proof

What Pythagoras did, though, was give
a proof. It was probably not the first
proof. And there have been numerous
proofs since – probably more than
for any other mathematical idea. But
Pythagoras's stuck, and so did the
idea that theories need proof. Indeed
proof has become the cornerstone
of maths, and searches for
proofs can stretch over

many centuries, as famously with Fermat's Last Theorem (see page 165).

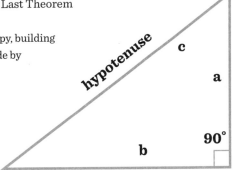

Pythagoras by all accounts was rather a hippy, building a commune in Sicily. His followers had to abide by some curious rules. They were not allowed to touch white feathers, nor to 'make water' in the sunshine. Eating beans was forbidden; Pythagoras believed in reincarnation, and was apparently worried that he might be reincarnated as a bean. And he was always looking for mathematical beauty in nature. This is what led him to look at how musical sounds are made, and he discovered how different pitches have a mathematical relationship. A harp string with twice the tension, for instance, gives a note twice as high. Pythagoras even believed the stars and planets revolved with a particular note.

It was this spiritual search for mathematical patterns in the world that led him to squares. He played with arrangements of stones in regular patterns. Pebbles in rows of equal numbers created a square. It might be two pebbles by two pebbles, or three by three. The number of pebbles in the square was therefore the 'square' of the number of pebbles in each side. Two by two is four, three by three is nine, and so on.

Playing with shapes

He likely arrived at his proof about right-angle triangles by playing with shapes in the same way as he did with stones. Indeed, Pythagoras's proof is often called a proof by rearrangement to distinguish it from other proofs.

It is simple: draw one smaller square inside another tilted at an angle so that its corners touch all four sides of the square. There are now four right-angled triangles inside each corner of the larger square. The smaller square forms the hypotenuse of each triangle.

If you rearrange the triangles into pairs, with the hypotenuse of each adjoining, you get two rectangles. Put these two rectangles inside the square and you end up with two small squares as well as the rectangles. Since the area of the triangles

Euclid's proof
of Pythagoras's
theorem

has not changed, the area of the square in the first arrangement must be equal to the area of the two small squares in the second arrangement. In other words, the square in the first arrangement is the hypotenuse; the squares in the second arrangement is the square of the other two sides. So the square of the hypotenuse equals the square on the other two sides.

A lasting impact

It was wonderfully simple, and completely incontrovertible. Nonetheless, mathematicians who came after Pythagoras wanted a more mathematical proof, not simple rearrangements of cutouts. In his great geometry book *Elements*, from around 300 BCE, Euclid devised a rather more sophisticated proof, using theoretical geometric logic rather than rearrangements. He drew an imaginary square on each side of a right-angle triangle. He then created imaginary congruent (matching) triangles between the corners of the squares and the triangles. Using these, he could go through a series of logical steps that showed the theorem must be correct. Euclid's theoretical proof has set the pattern for geometrical proofs ever since.

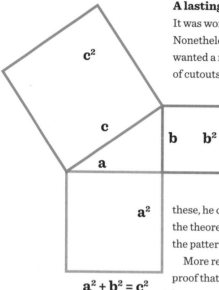
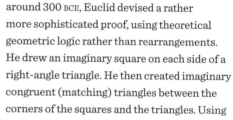

More recently, though, Einstein came up with an ingenious proof that involved cutting up the triangle like Pythagoras, but no rearrangement at all, while other mathematicians have come up with entirely algebraic proofs.

The theorem also led to the discovery of irrational numbers, which cannot be denoted as a ratio of integers. A right-angled triangle with sides of one unit would have a hypotenuse of square root two. This discovery contradicted the Pythagoreans' fundamental belief in the rationality of all numbers. The legend famously goes that Hippasus, who proved that the square root of two was irrational, was drowned for his discovery.

Beyond pure mathematics, right-angled triangles are used to measure the steepness of mountains, the slope of roofs or to ensure that two walls meet at a right angle. Its simplicity is iconic, yet it is arguably the most important and widely used mathematical formula.

HOW BIG
IS INFINITY?

THE MATHS OF THE VERY LARGE
AND THE VERY SMALL

ca 400 BCE

ASSOCIATED
MATHEMATICIANS:
Ancient Greeks

CONCLUSION:
The Greeks toyed with
infinity, but in recent times
mathematicians have found
it to be more complicated
than anyone imagined.

The idea of infinity is difficult to understand. As humans with a finite lifespan, used to dealing with concrete, finite objects, how can we get to grips with the concept of something that goes on forever?

The ancient Greeks and infinity

Several of the ancient Greek mathematicians wrestled with the concept of infinity. Euclid proved there was an infinite number of prime numbers. Aristotle also realized that time goes on forever, with no end. The Greeks called infinity *apeiron*, which means 'without bounds', or without end. They disliked the idea, because they preferred to deal with (small) whole numbers.

The philosopher Zeno famously used infinite ideas in several paradoxes in the fifth century BCE. The most well known of these paradoxes is Achilles and the tortoise, in which Achilles, a famous warrior from Greek mythology, races a tortoise. Let's say he gives the tortoise a 50-metre head start in a 100-metre race. The race begins, and Achilles sets off like a bullet; in five seconds he has covered 50-metres, and has reached the place where the tortoise started. The tortoise, however, has also been sprinting, or perhaps waddling, and has covered half a metre; so it is now half a metre in the lead.

Achilles runs this half metre in 0.05 seconds, but once again the tortoise has been waddling, and has moved on by 5 millimetres, and is still in the lead. In fact every time Achilles reaches the point where the tortoise was, it has moved forward. This carries on for an infinite number of catch-ups, each getting smaller. So Achilles can never reach the tortoise.

Are all infinities the same?

More than 1,500 years later, Italian scientist Galileo worried about the size of infinities. Are they all the same, or is there a variety? For example, every integer has a square: $1^2 = 1$, $2^2 = 4$, $3^2 = 9$, and so on. Most integers are not squares (2, 3, 5, 6, 7, for example), so there are clearly more integers than squares. There is an infinite number of integers, and an infinite number of squares; so the infinity of integers should be greater than the infinity of squares. But every integer is the square root of a square, which suggests that you could match every integer with a square – in other words there is a one-to-one correspondence between integers and squares, so the two infinities should be the same. This is known as Galileo's paradox.

Galileo concluded that 'the attributes "equal", "greater", and "less" are only applicable to finite quantities'.

Different sizes of infinity

German mathematician Georg Ferdinand Ludwig Philipp Cantor (1845–1918) went even further, defining different sizes of infinity.

There is, for example, a set of all the integral (or natural) numbers: 1, 2, 3, 4, and so on. There is the set of all even numbers: 2, 4, 6, 8, etc. Even numbers can be placed in one-to-one correspondence with the integers: $2 \rightarrow 1$, $4 \rightarrow 2$, $6 \rightarrow 3$, $8 \rightarrow 4$, and this means that the even numbers are countable. Further, the infinity of even numbers is the same as the infinity of odd numbers and the infinity of all integers.

There is also a set of all the real numbers, such as 1.0, 1.1, 1.01, 1.001, 1.0001, and so on. Cantor showed that the set of real numbers is uncountable, because they cannot be put in one-to-one correspondence with integers. Therefore the set of real numbers is greater than the set of integers, which led to the idea that there are many possible sizes for infinite sets. This seems intuitively obvious, since there is clearly an infinity of real numbers between 1 and 2, but Cantor managed to prove it.

Using infinity

Infinity may be hard to imagine, and even harder to pin down. And yet mathematicians have had to learn to deal with it – though nineteenth-century German mathematician Leopold Kronecker insisted that it was too much of a vague notion to have any place in maths!

Calculus, for instance, has to deal with infinitesimals – infinitely small divisions. There is no one point where time stops or things cease to move, for instance. The only way to work with this infinitely divisible continuum is to create limits, and assume the point you are interested in is midway between these limits. In the same way, the structure of a fractal is reiterated in ever smaller detail as you magnify it. The sequence stretches into infinity, and smaller details are simply smoothed out by the limits to resolution.

The Koch snowflake

The very difficulty of the concept of infinity, though, has kept it at forefront of mathematical thinking – becoming, for instance, the focus of whether things in maths are provable or not provable. In the wake of Kurt Gödel's incompleteness theorems (see page 142), it seems we should live with the idea of not everything in maths being ultimately provable. On the other hand, German mathematician David Hilbert introduced the famous Grand Hotel paradox in the 1924. In Hilbert's Hotel, all the infinite numbers of rooms are fully occupied. Yet by an ingenious series of proofs, Hilbert showed that rooms for infinitely more guests can always be found. Intuitively, this is nonsense. How can you find spaces in a hotel that is already full? But this is the paradox of infinity. Hilbert's proof is watertight. It just proves intuition and common sense can be wrong...

CHAPTER 2: Problems and solutions:
399 BCE – CE 628

The ancient Greeks revelled in the ideas of pure mathematics, in constructing diagrams with straight edges and compasses, especially in the field of geometry. Gradually, however, they turned their attention to specific problems, and tried to solve them with the mathematical insights they had amassed.

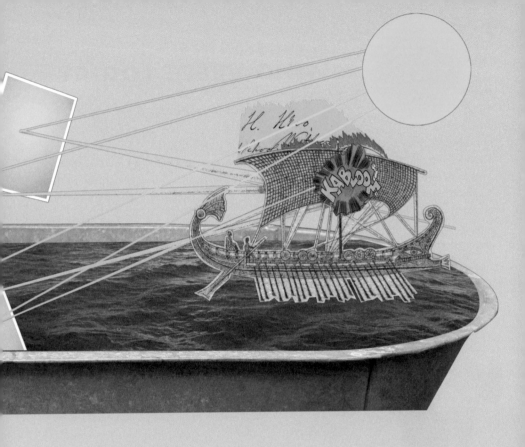

One of the most impressive of these Greeks was Archimedes, who exhibited an extraordinary range of talents, from the purest in mathematics to the most practical in physics and engineering. Others followed him, extending not only their understanding of the world about them but also how to manipulate it to their advantage.

ASSOCIATED
MATHEMATICIAN:

Euclid

WHO NEEDS LOGIC?

EUCLID'S *ELEMENTS*

CONCLUSION:

Euclid's collection of
mathematical propositions
and proofs was so clear
and logical that it has been
used as a textbook of
geometry for 2,000 years.

Written about 2300 years ago, Euclid's great book *Elements* is
sometimes said to be the most widely read book in the western
world after the Bible. It's just a maths book, but what a book it is!

The original textbook

It's essentially a textbook about geometry: the mathematics
of shape. It wasn't even the first geometry book. But it is so
complete, and so thorough in its methodology that it has
provided the basic framework for geometry ever since.
Even now, the geometry of flat surfaces – lines,
points, shapes and solids – is described as
Euclidean geometry. The essential rules about
triangles, squares, circles, parallel lines and so
on are all in the pages of Euclid.
But it would be a mistake to think of
Elements as just a really good schoolbook; it
launched a profound new way of thinking about
the world. In Euclid's system, the workings of
the world are not just the whims of the gods,
but follow natural rules. It showed how we
can find our way to the truth through logic
and deductive reasoning, evidence and proof
– not just intuition. The idea of presenting
theories and proofs is the basis of all science today.
Euclid wasn't alone. His work is the culmination of
centuries of intellectual effort by Greek thinkers, dating
back to Thales of Miletus. Yet Euclid's work brought it
together with lasting power and precision.
Not much is known about Euclid. Indeed, like
Pythagoras he may not have been a single person but
a group of mathematics teachers in Alexandria, the great
city then newly founded by Alexander the Great on

Egypt's Mediterranean coast. Endowed with a remarkable library by Ptolemy, the first Greek king there, it became an intellectual powerhouse.

Practical maths and eternal truths

By the time of Euclid, geometry was already a highly developed practical skill. People had long used it to work out the area of their land or how to build a perfect pyramid. But what Euclid and his fellow ancient Greeks did was develop these hands-on techniques into a purely theoretical system, turning 'applied maths' into 'pure maths'.

This wasn't just an academic exercise; the Greek method was a powerful tool for finding underlying truths. What was true of triangles in one situation was true in a completely different situation. When Thales of Miletus went to Egypt, he amazed them by showing how the method of similar triangles could be used to measure both the height of the pyramids and the distance of a ship at sea.

Euclid and the Greeks unleashed the lasting power of mathematics by turning it into a complete logic system. As Euclid showed, it came with proofs, and the idea that rules could be worked out logically from certain assumptions, or postulates, such as 'A straight line is the shortest distance between two points'. Assumptions are combined to make a basic idea for a rule, called a theorem, which then must be proved or disproved.

At the heart of Euclid's *Elements* are five key axioms:

1. A line can be drawn between two given points.

2. Such a line can be extended indefinitely in either direction.

3. A circle can be drawn with any radius with any given point at its centre.

4. All right angles are equal.

5. If a line crosses two other lines so that the inner angles on the same side add up to less than two right angles, then the two lines it crosses must eventually meet.

The first four sound self-evident now, yet they were not at the time. It was absolutely fundamental to lay down ground rules for the basics. Only with unarguable

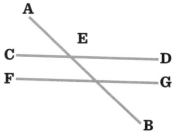

Euclid's fifth postulate

definitions of the basics can we turn hunches into firm proofs and move logically forward through each step.

The problem of the fifth postulate

The fifth postulate is less self-evident. It's sometimes called the parallel postulate. The idea is that when a line crosses two other lines so that the inner angles on the same side add up to two right angles, then the two lines it crosses must be parallel. This postulate is central to all basic geometric constructions, and has numerous practical applications. It's essential for making parallel lines for trains to run on, for instance.

Yet Euclid rightly had doubts about the parallel postulate. His geometry works perfectly for flat, two- or three-dimensional surfaces and most everyday situations. But just like the Earth's surface is curved, so is space. It also has more than three dimensions, including time.

Euclid's parallel postulate means that only one line can be drawn parallel to another through a given point. But if space is curved and multidimensional, then many other parallel lines can be drawn. That was the thinking behind the creation of 'hyperbolic' geometry by mathematicians such as Janos Bolyai and Bernhard Riemann in the nineteenth century.

Similarly, according to Euclid's geometry, the internal angles of a triangle always add up to 180 degrees – yet those of a triangle drawn on a ball add up to more than 180 degrees. Over the last two centuries, therefore, mathematicians have begun to develop a new geometry for curved and multidimensional space that goes beyond Euclid. These new geometries proved crucial for the ideas behind Einstein's General Theory of Relativity. Nonetheless, Euclid's work remains central to all everyday geometry today.

HOW MANY PRIME NUMBERS ARE THERE?

EUCLID'S PROOF BY CONTRADICTION

ca 300 BCE

ASSOCIATED
MATHEMATICIANS:
Euclid

CONCLUSION:
There are an infinite
number of primes.

For most people a number is just a way of saying 'how many'. But for many mathematicians, numbers are fascinating in their own right. The study of numbers, number theory, is said to be the queen of mathematics, the purest most abstract intellectual pursuit. Within the field of number theory, 'primes' are the gold standard, catnip to number theorists, and have been ever since Euclid talked about them 2,300 years ago in *Elements*, his great book about geometry.

The mathematical key to the universe

To many mathematicians, a complete understanding of primes is like the Holy Grail of numbers. They are often described as the 'atoms' of numbers, the fundamental particles from which everything is built. In his 1985 book *Contact*, Carl Sagan suggested that prime numbers would be the best way to communicate with intelligent beings from other worlds, because knowledge of primes must be a universal sign of intelligent life.

A prime is a number that has two distinct factors, itself and one. In Book VII of *Elements*, Euclid described any number as being 'a multitude of units' – that is, many ones – which is about as simple an abstract definition of a number as you can get. He defined a prime number as a number 'measured by a unit alone' – that is, it can only be divided by one, which he didn't count as a number. He also defined a composite number as a number that is not a prime: composite because it can be created by multiplying other primes. A perfect number, he said, was a number that equals the sum of its divisors.

Euclid made interesting comments about both composite and perfect numbers, but it is his proof about prime numbers that was the real game changer. He wanted to know just how many prime numbers there are. His elegant proof that there is in fact no limit to the number of primes is laid out in Book IX as Proposition 20, and signalled the birth of number theory. Although Pythagoras and other Greek mathematicians had also been interested in prime numbers, Proposition 20 was groundbreaking because it used a proof, and so set the pattern for the study of numbers throughout history.

Euclid's proof

Euclid's proof is what is now called 'a proof by contradiction' – that is, it starts out by assuming the opposite of what you want to prove, then sets out a series of logical steps showing it is actually impossible.

The proposition Euclid wanted to prove was that there are more than any finite number of primes – that is, there is an infinite number of primes. In other words, he wanted to show that there is not a finite number of primes. So he started, in the method of contradiction, by assuming that there is a finite number, then set out to show this was impossible. His disproof hinged on the assumption that every natural number is the product of prime numbers.

The original in Greek is not so easy to follow. But this is the gist of it. If there is a finite number of primes, you should be able to make a list of them all, p_1, p_2, p_3, all the way up to p_n, the highest-number prime. Now what if you multiply all the numbers in the list together and add 1? You don't have to actually do this, but just follow the logic.

The resulting number can't be a prime, because it's bigger than the biggest prime on our list. So it must be a composite number. But a composite number is the product of prime numbers. So you should be able to divide it by prime numbers. But you can't do this without getting a remainder of 1. So our list of prime numbers cannot be complete; there must be prime numbers that are not on our supposedly complete list.

It doesn't matter what your biggest prime is, the result will always be the same; there must always be bigger primes. The ingenuity of this argument is breathtaking, and it has inspired countless mathematicians to search for similar logical proofs and pathways through the forest of numbers.

An infinite search for infinity

Indeed, mathematicians have tried their hands at other proofs that primes are infinite. Leonhard Euler came up with a proof in the eighteenth century, Hungarian mathematician Paul Erdős came up with another arithmetic proof in the 1950s, and American-Israeli mathematician Hillel Furstenberg devised a proof based on set theory. In just the last decade, more than half a dozen new proofs have been presented, including Alexander Shen's 2016 idea based on information theory, and 'compressibility states'.

Yet despite this proof that primes are infinite, it has not deterred mathematicians from a relentless - and by definition, eternal - search for them. Not long after Euclid, another great Greek, Eratosthenes came up with a method for identifying primes with a clever mathematical sieve that quickly sifted out non-primes, while in the 1800s Carl Friedrich Gauss discovered a rule that showed that primes become less and less frequent as numbers get bigger. Still the hunt goes on, but it all began with Euclid.

ca 250 BCE

ASSOCIATED MATHEMATICIAN:

Archimedes

CONCLUSION:

Archimedes used an ingenious method to work out a useful estimate of pi.

WHAT IS PI?

FINDING THE LIMITS OF PI

For geometers, a circle is a frustrating thing. When shapes have straight sides, calculations are straightforward. Want to know the area of a rectangle? Just multiply the length by the width. Or the area of an equilateral triangle? That's simply half the base times the height. But circles are an entirely different issue. For circles, you have to bring in one of the most aggravating figures in all maths, pi.

The pi problem

Pi is the circumference of a circle with a diameter of one or, to put it another way, it's the ratio of the circumference to the diameter of any circle. It sounds simple, but it is actually an astonishingly elusive figure. Calculating it has defeated some of the finest mathematical brains in history, and even the massed computing power of the modern world has not managed to pin it down precisely.

Fortunately, an approximation is good enough for most practical purposes. People have known since ancient times that it is just over three – in other words, the circumference of a circle is just over three times as long as its diameter. Clay tablets from Babylon, dating back almost 4,000 years, suggest that the ancient Babylonians thought pi was 25/8 – that is, 3.125, which is close to the modern estimate of close to 3.142. Meanwhile, the ancient Egyptian Rhind papyrus from around the same time suggests a figure of 16/9 squared – that is, 256/81 or 3.16.

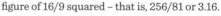

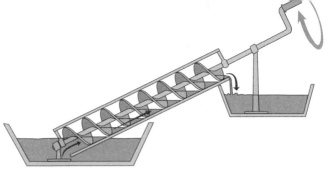

A genius of the ancient world

In about 250 BCE, the great genius of the ancient world, Archimedes, set out to find an accurate answer. Archimedes was a legend in his own lifetime, known mostly for his amazing inventions and for his achievements in science. Among his more impressive accomplishments, he once pushed a small lever to launch a 4,000-ton ship, *Syracusa*, singlehandedly with his ingenious pulley-driven device. The Archimedes screw, a simple pumping device, is still used today for irrigation and for pumping thick, sludgy liquids like sewage. And of course, it was Archimedes who discovered the laws of buoyancy, famously announced, so the story goes, with his legendary cry of 'Eureka!' ('I have found it!')

But he was also a brilliant mathematician, and in some ways, his calculation of pi is one of his most significant achievements. What makes it important is that Archimedes did not try to measure pi; he tried to work it out theoretically. His idea was to use the 'method of exhaustion' invented by the philosopher Antiphon about 480 BCE, and developed by the great Greek mathematician Eudoxus a century later. The idea was to find the area of a shape that was hard to calculate by filling it up gradually with polygons whose area you did know. You started with big polygons, then filled in the gap with ever-smaller polygons until the space inside the shape was 'exhausted'. It was only ever an approximation, but the smaller the polygons, the more accurate it got. The method is a precursor to calculus.

Hexagoning the circle

It was this method Archimedes used to calculate pi. Archimedes' notes are hard to follow, but this, in essence, is what he did. First he drew a circle with a compass and then,

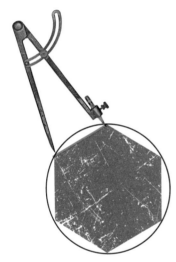

keeping the compass at the same radius, he marked out six equally spaced points along the circle's circumference. By drawing a line between each neighbouring point, he created a hexagon inside the circle, and by drawing a line between opposite corners of the hexagon, he created six equilateral triangles, with sides matching the radius of the circle.

So the perimeter of the hexagon must be six times the radius of the circle, or three times its diameter. So we've already got an approximate value for pi of 3. But the circle curves round outside the hexagon, so the real value of pi must be greater. So Archimedes drew small, shallow, equilateral triangles on the outer edges of the hexagon, creating a dodecahedron, a figure with 12 sides. There was still a gap, so Archimedes went on, making a figure with 24 sides, then 48, then 96. The 96-sided figure is almost indistinguishable from a circle and gave a figure of 3 and 10/71 or 223/71 (3.140845).

But then came Archimedes's real stroke of genius; he repeated the process to draw a hexagon outside the circle, doubling its sides until he got a 96-sided figure. This gave a figure of 3 and 10/70 or 220/70 (3.142857). Since the circle lay in between, he could be sure the value of pi lies between his inner figure and his outer figure. This would have given him a figure of 3.141851, which is very, very close indeed to today's figure for pi of approximately 3.14159. Of course, Archimedes did not have the benefit of decimals, and so people took his outer value of 22/7, and this is still the approximation that most of us use today.

Since Archimedes's time, pi has been calculated ever more accurately, and with high-powered computers, values of pi can be worked out to trillions of decimal places. Yet, there is still no end-point, no final definitive number that we can categorically call pi, since it's an irrational number (see page 21). We simply get closer approximations, and Archimedes' approximation of 22/7 is all the pi most of us ever need.

HOW BIG IS
THE EARTH?

SUN, SHADOWS AND GREEK GEOMETRY

ca 240 BCE

ASSOCIATED
MATHEMATICIAN:
Eratosthenes

CONCLUSION:
Eratosthenes used a
clever mathematical trick
to calculate the Earth's
circumference to be
25,000 miles.

In 332 BCE Alexander the Great founded the Greek city of
Alexandria, at the mouth of the Nile in Egypt. Alexandria
became the centre of learning in the Greek world, and a
magnificent library was built up, containing hundreds of
thousands of scrolls made from parchment or vellum. Around
240 BCE a new librarian was appointed – Eratosthenes of
Cyrene, a mathematician who devised a method of finding
prime numbers (see page 37). As librarian, Eratosthenes was
energetic, borrowing great works of literature, having them
copied and then (on Ptolemy's orders) returning the copies,
while retaining the originals.

Eratosthenes was born around 276 BCE and became friends
with his contemporary Archimedes, even though they lived
at opposite ends of the Mediterranean. Archimedes sent
Eratosthenes a poem describing a complex problem about
cows and bulls, and probably visited him in Alexandria.

Father of geography

Eratosthenes was such an all-rounder that his critics
sometimes called him 'Beta', because he was second-best
at everything. His friends, however, called him 'Pentathlos':
the pentathlete, the all-round champion. Not only a
mathematician, he was also a poet and astronomer, and he
invented the science of geography.

He wrote three volumes on geography, in which he drew
maps of the whole world, including the poles, the tropics and
the temperate zones in between. He included the locations
of 400 cities.

The ancient Greeks knew that the Earth was round;
they had two solid pieces of evidence. First, when a

ship sailed away from the shore, it gradually disappeared from the bottom up. Clearly the ship was not just getting too small to see, but was going *over* the horizon, which meant that the Earth had to be round. Second, they realized that an eclipse of the moon was caused by the shadow of the Earth, and this shadow was curved.

Measuring the Earth

Knowing that the Earth was a sphere, Eratosthenes wanted to find out its diameter.

Eight hundred kilometres (500 miles) south of Alexandria, near the border with what is now Sudan, lay the town of Syene (now Aswan). Here on Elephant Island in the Nile there is a well. Eratosthenes knew that at noon on midsummer's day anyone who looked down the well could see a reflection of the sun, unless it was blocked by the shadow of his head. This had to mean that the sun was exactly overhead at that time. The well is still there, but unfortunately it is now dry and full of rubble.

Back in Alexandria, Eratosthenes planted a gnomon (stick) vertically in the ground, and at noon on midsummer's day measured the angle of the sun, or rather the angle between the stick and the edge of its shadow; it was 7.2°. This is the angle A in the diagram opposite.

This was the same as the angle A*, because these two angles are on either side of a diagonal between parallel lines. A* is the angle at the centre of the Earth between Alexandria and Syene; so Eratosthenes was able to make this simple calculation.

Angle between Alexandria and Syene = 7.2°

Distance from Alexandria to Syene = 500 miles

Angle all round Earth from Alexandria to Alexandria = 360°

= 50 × 7.2°

Therefore, distance round the Earth = 50 x 500 = 25,000 miles. The distance from Alexandria to Syene had been measured by official *bematistoi* (surveyors who had been trained to pace evenly and count their paces), and Eratosthenes gave his result in *stades*, rather than miles. We don't know exactly how long the stade was, but as far as we know, his estimate of the circumference of the Earth was close to today's accurate value of 24,900 miles.

In his calculation, Eratosthenes assumed that Syene was on the tropic of Cancer, that it was due south of Alexandria and that the Earth is a perfect sphere. None of these assumptions is precisely accurate. Nevertheless, the experiment was repeated in 2012 using more accurate data; the result was 24,901 miles.

Eratosthenes went on to calculate the tilt of the Earth's axis (about 23°) and invented the leap day (now 29 February). He built an armillary sphere – a model of the Earth surrounded on rings by the sun, moon and other celestial objects. He also calculated (not very accurately) the distance to the sun, and its diameter. Sadly, most of his work on the many academic disciplines he contributed to was lost following the destruction by fire of much of the Great Library of Alexandria in 48 BCE.

Calculating the distance around the Earth

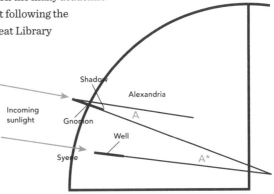

ca CE 250

**ASSOCIATED
MATHEMATICIAN:**

Diophantus of Alexandria

CONCLUSION:
Diophantus was likely
the first person to use
a symbol such as *x* to
stand for a number.

HOW OLD WAS THE FATHER OF ALGEBRA?

USING LETTERS IN SUMS

Diophantus of Alexandria is a rather shadowy figure. We do not know when he lived, and can only guess he was born in the early 200s and active around CE 250.

He has been called the 'father of algebra' because he seems to have been the first person to represent numbers by letters in order to solve equations. As far as he could he used whole numbers, but he did admit that simple fractions were also numbers.

How old?

The *Greek Anthology* of CE 500 contains a puzzle about Diophantus's age when he died: 'His boyhood lasted 1/6th of his life; his beard grew after 1/12th more; he married after 1/7th more, and his son was born five years later; the son lived to half his father's age, and the father died four years after the son.'

One way to solve this puzzle is to use his algebra, with a Diophantine equation. Let x be his age when he died.

Then we can write the puzzle as $x = x/6 + x/12 + x/7 + 5 + x/2 + 4$

This comes out to: $9x = 756$, or $x = 84$

Another way to solve the puzzle is to recognize that Diophantus liked to use only integers. It follows that his age must have been divisible by 12 and by 7; $12 \times 7 = 84$. Try this on the rest of the puzzle and it all works out neatly.

Arithmetica

Diophantus wrote 13 volumes of a book called *Arithmetica*, of which only six survive. They describe 130 problems, giving numerical solutions.

Arithmetica was the first serious work on algebra, and had immense influence not only on Greek mathematics but also on Arab and later Western mathematics. In addition to using a symbol for the unknown quantity, Diophantus used a symbol for 'equals' (not our equals sign =, for which we have English mathematician Robert Recorde to thank).

Diophantus's equations were mostly quadratic, involving x^2 and x in some form. For us, such equations have two solutions. For example, the equation

$x^2 + 2x = 3$

can be solved to give

$x = 1$ or $x = -3$

But Diophantus never bothered to look for more than one solution (or 'root'), and would have ignored any negative number as meaningless or absurd. This is logical if you think of numbers as cardinal numbers used for counting objects; there is no such quantity as –3 apples. Furthermore, he had no concept of zero.

Despite these slight drawbacks, Diophantus was essentially the founder of algebra, and at the same time made major advances in number theory. He became immensely famous when a French mathematician read a copy of *Arithmetica*.

Fermat's Last Theorem

Centuries after the death of Diophantus, *Arithmetica* was to inspire one of mathematics' most famous theorems. Pierre de Fermat, born in 1607, was a French lawyer at the Parlement de Toulouse, and a gifted amateur mathematician. He made several significant advances in mathematics, and his conjectures generally proved to be correct.

In *Arithmetica*, Diophantus discussed Pythagoras's theorem (see page 26). This involves the equation

$$x^2 + y^2 = z^2$$

which has infinite integer solutions. In the margin of his copy of the book, Fermat scribbled (in Latin)

It is impossible for a cube to be written as the sum of two cubes, or a fourth power to be written as the sum of two fourth powers or, in general, for any number which is a power greater than the second to be written as a sum of two like powers.

In other words, Fermat had extended the Pythagorean equation to

$$x^n + y^n = z^n$$

and asserted that there were no integral solutions if n was greater than two. He then wrote, 'I have a truly marvellous demonstration of this proposition, which this margin is too narrow to contain.' Fermat scribbled this in about 1637, but did not publish it, and told no one. He had a habit of making such assertions without proof and he was usually right. He died in 1665, but in 1670 his son published a collection of his work, and in due course mathematicians the world over fell on this particular problem and began looking for a proof. This irritating little puzzle became known as Fermat's Last Theorem.

Thousands of pounds worth of prizes were offered for a solution, and thousands of wrong answers were submitted. Still mathematicians beavered away, until in 1994 British mathematician Andrew Wiles, after struggling with the puzzle for 30 years, came up with a long and complex solution (see page 165).

Wiles used some advanced modern mathematics that Fermat could not have known. So did Fermat really have a truly marvellous demonstration? We may never know.

WHAT IS NOTHING?

THE VALUE OF ZERO

CE **628**

ASSOCIATED
MATHEMATICIAN:
Brahmagupta

CONCLUSION:
Early mathematicians had
no concept of zero as a
number, even though some
used a place-value system,
and used a symbol for zero
as a placeholder.

The word *zero* comes from the Arabic *sifr*, meaning empty.
Fibonacci introduced the decimal system to Europe and
translated *sifr* as *zephyrum*, which became *zefiro* in Italian,
and was shortened in Venice to zero.

We use a place-value system of numbers; the symbols 321
mean three hundreds, two tens, and one unit: total three
hundred and twenty-one. The value of each digit depends on its
place in the string. The CE 500 Sanskrit astronomical treatise
Aryabhatiya defines the place-value system thus 'From place to
place each is 10 times the preceding.'

Is zero a number?

Zero is unique. Sometimes it's a number, as in the answer to
'How many apples are there in the bowl?' 'Zero (or none).'
Sometimes it's a placeholder, as in the number 203; the zero is
there to show there are no tens. Without the placeholder
the number would be 23. It holds the place in the
tens column.

For thousands of years people had no
need for zero; it is not needed for counting
objects, or people or days. If you had three
nuts and you took away three nuts, there
was nothing left; you did not need a
number. Nor is it needed as an ordinal
number for labelling things: the first in
the queue, or the second Thursday of
the month.

The ancient Greeks had no zero. They
worried about whether nothing was a
number; how could nothing be something?

They used letters of the alphabet for numerical digits, but by AD 130 Ptolemy, in his astronomy book the *Almagest*, was using a symbol like this, ō, for zero.

Several ancient civilizations developed place-value systems, including the Babylonians and the Egyptians, who used a symbol for zero. Some left an empty space, which could lead to confusion in handwritten numbers such as 2 3; is that meant to be 203, 2,003 or 20,003? The Olmecs in Mesoamerica used characters for placeholders in their Long Count calendars.

Roman numerals are fine for counting – in fact, they are essentially a tally system – but they are hopeless for calculations. For mathematical operations you need a place-value system, and preferably a zero.

Inventing zero

According to legend, the first person to investigate zero in writing was a young Indian mathematician called Brahmagupta, who was born in 598, and later became director of an astronomical observatory. In his 628 book *Brahmasphuṭasiddhanta* (*The Improved Treatise of Brahma*) he wrote in verse (in Sanskrit) about the movements of the planets and the calculation of their paths, using zero as a placeholder. More than that, however, he showed how to use zero as a number.

To make sure everyone understood what he was talking about, he defined zero as 'the result of subtracting a number from itself'. Then he gave the first precise rules for using the number zero in arithmetical operations:

> *The sum of two positives is positive, of two negatives negative; of a positive and a negative the sum is their difference; if they are equal it is zero. The sum of a negative and zero is negative, that of a positive and zero positive, of two zeros zero... The product of zero and a negative, of zero and a positive, or of two zeros is zero.*

His conclusions about division by zero, however, differ from ours. He said that 0/0 is 0, and skated over what is meant by any other number divided by zero. The trouble is that if you take four and divide it by two you get two; divide four by one you get four; divide four by half you get eight; divide four by one hundredth you get 400. As the number you are dividing by gets smaller and smaller the answer gets bigger and bigger. So does dividing by zero give you infinity? No, not really, for multiplying infinity by zero still does not give you four. Furthermore, if dividing one by zero gives you infinity, and dividing two by zero gives you infinity, then one = two. Aaargh! Dividing by zero is really meaningless, or 'indeterminate'. Zero is a strange animal.

The acceptance of zero

From India the idea of zero spread to Mesopotamia, where Arab mathematicians realized its importance. From there it spread to the West; the 'Arabic' numerals we use now were actually Hindu numerals filtered through Mesopotamia.

Following Georg Cantor's invention of set theory (see page 30) mathematicians today define zero as the empty set. As British mathematician Ian Stewart wittily puts it, 'This is a collection that doesn't actually contain anything, such as my own collection of vintage Rolls-Royces.' The empty set becomes a cornerstone for the whole of mathematics.

Zero is the integer (whole number) between –1 and +1. It is an even number, because it is divisible by two with no remainder. It is neither negative nor positive. It is not a prime number, because any number multiplied by zero is zero. Trying to divide any real number by zero is meaningless, because the answer is indeterminate.

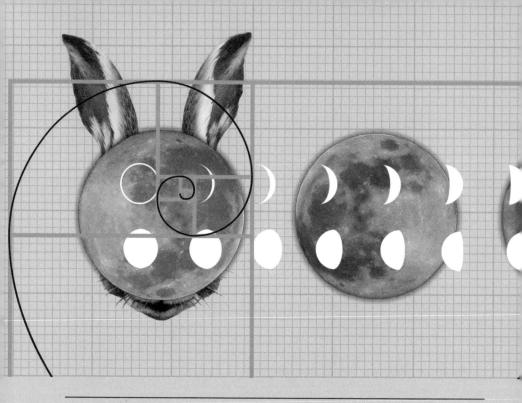

CHAPTER 3: Rabbits and Reality: 629 – 1665

Numbers and mathematics were derived from observing the world around us, like counting the days in a lunar cycle or measuring the size of a mountain or a field. Throughout history, mathematicians never stopped using the real world to drive their work. Rabbits inspired Fibonacci's most famous contribution to mathematics. A fly on his ceiling famously spurred Descartes' mathematical brilliance.

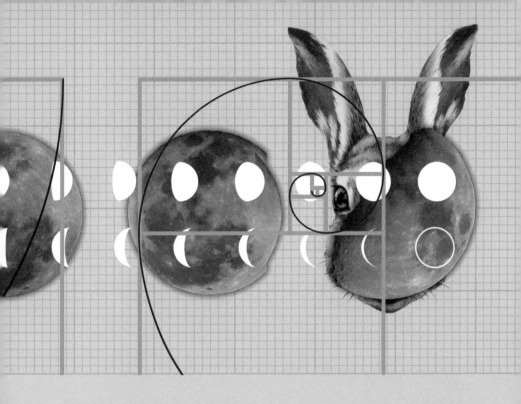

Yet, the acceptance of zero changed everything. How could zero – nothing, the absence of anything real – be a quantity? Now maths didn't have to limit itself to the real world. Mathematicians learned how to deal with what didn't exist. Bombelli realized that imaginary numbers both have to and can't be real. And the idea of the infinitely small led Kepler, and later Newton and Leibniz, to their massive breakthroughs in the seventeenth century.

ASSOCIATED
MATHEMATICIAN:

al-Khwarizmi

CONCLUSION:
During the Golden Age
of Islam mathematics
changed direction.

CAN YOU DO SUMS WITHOUT NUMBERS?

SOLVING QUADRATIC EQUATIONS

The Qur'an, the sacred book of Islam, is almost unique among major religious books in encouraging the study of science. The faithful are urged to observe such things as the flight of birds and the falling of rain, and this endorsement of scientific study had a lasting effect on the unravelling of the secrets of nature.

The House of Wisdom

By CE 750, the Islamic empire stretched from Spain all the way across North Africa to Arabia, Syria and Persia, stopping at the River Indus in modern-day Pakistan. Harun al-Rashid became the fifth Caliph of the Abbasid dynasty on 14 September 786; he brought culture to his court and looked to establish intellectual disciplines. He died in 809 and his younger son, al-Mamun, became caliph. In 830, al-Mamun founded an academy called the House of Wisdom, where Greek philosophical and scientific works were translated into Arabic, and started building up a library of manuscripts.

Into this golden age of Islam came a young Persian, who may have been born around 780 in what is now Uzbekistan; his name was Muhammad ibn Mūsā al-Khwārizmī, generally abbreviated to al-Khwarizmi. Under the patronage of al-Mamun he wrote books on mathematics, geography and astronomy, and became head of the library in the House of Wisdom in Baghdad.

Hindu numerals

His popular book, *On the Calculation with Hindu Numerals*, written around 820, was principally responsible for spreading the Indian numbering system throughout the Middle East and Europe (see page 17). He showed how to do calculations with these strange numerals, and introduced tricks for solving problems. For example:

If three men can plant a crop in five days, how quickly can four men do it? Write the relevant numbers down:

3 5 4

Then multiply the first by the second (3 × 5 = 15), then divide by the third (15/4) and the answer is 3 ¾ or 3.75 days.

The father of algebra

Al-Khwarizmi's book on algebra demonstrated the first systematic solutions of linear and quadratic equations. One of al-Khwarizmi's principal achievements in algebra was showing how to solve quadratic equations by completing the square. To solve the equation $x^2 + 10x = 39$, for example, he constructs the square on x, then draws rectangles against the sides, each x long and 10/4 = 5/2 wide, so that their total area is 10x. We know that the area of the square plus these rectangles is 39.

He then completes the square by adding four corner squares of 25/4 each, making a total area for the big square of 39 + 25, or 64. The side of the big square is therefore $\sqrt{64}$, or 8, which means that x, the side of the middle square, is (8 − 2 × 5/2) or 3. The solution is x = 3.

This was the first book to treat algebra as an independent

discipline, and it introduced the methods of *al-jabr* and *al-muqabala*. The word *al-jabr* means 'reduction', or 'the mending of broken bones'. From this comes our word algebra. This first step in solving equations was to get rid of any negative units and roots from any equation, by adding the same to each side. So $x^2 = 10x - 5x^2$ is reduced to $6x^2 = 10x$.

Al-muqabala means bringing together things of the same type. So $x^2 + 25 = x - 3$ is reduced to $x^2 + 28 = x$. He had to do this in words, however, since modern notation was far in the future. For example, he would say 'You divide ten into two parts: multiply the one by itself; it will be equal to the other taken eighty-one times', which in our notation would mean

$$(10 - x)^2 = 81x.$$

Al-Khwarizmi has been described (like Diophantus – see page 46) as the father of algebra. The Greek concept of mathematics was essentially about geometry. This new algebra allowed mathematicians to debate rational numbers, irrational numbers, and geometrical sizes.

Al-Khwarizmi was interested not only in pure mathematics, but in

> what is easiest and most useful in arithmetic, such as men constantly require in cases of inheritance, legacies, partition, lawsuits, and trade, and in all their dealings with one another, or where the measuring of lands, the digging of canals, geometrical computations, and other objects of various sorts and kinds are concerned.

His name al-Khwarizmi became the English 'algorithm', originally meaning how to operate with Arabic numerals, and now more generally a set of rules, commonly to solve calculations in computing, but also other procedures involving steps and method.

HOW MANY RABBITS?

NATURE'S NUMBER SEQUENCE

1202

ASSOCIATED
MATHEMATICIAN:
Fibonacci

CONCLUSION:
There is a number series
that shows up all the time
in maths, art and
the natural world.

Leonardo of Pisa was born around 1170, just before
construction of the famous leaning tower began in 1173.
He is generally known as Fibonacci, which is short for
Filius Bonacci (son of Bonacci). His father was a merchant
and customs officer. As a young man, Fibonacci travelled
extensively round the Mediterranean with him, and learned
about the 'Arabic' numbers, which had come from India (see
page 17). He also learned about various forms of arithmetic
from the merchants he met.

In 1202 he published an important book, *Liber Abaci* (*The
Book of Calculating*), which introduced the 'Arabic' numbers to
Europe. It also popularized a fascinating number sequence by
telling a story about rabbits.

The rabbits

Suppose a pair of baby rabbits come into a field. In the first
month they are too young to have babies, but by the end of
the second month they mature, and
produce a pair. These babies go on to
produce their own babies two months
later. Each new pair waits for two
months to have babies, and
then produces a pair every
month thereafter. So
the tribe gradually
expands.

**Fibonacci's
pairs of
breeding
rabbits**

Fibonacci asked how many pairs of rabbits will there be at the beginning of each month? For the first and second month the first pair are alone, but then their babies come, so there are now two pairs. During the next month the first pair produce another pair; there are now three pairs. Next month the second pair produce their own babies; the total by the following month jumps to five.

The sequence develops like this:

1, 1, 2, 3, 5, 8, 13, 21, 34, 55, 89, 144, 233, 377...

Each number is generated by adding together the two previous numbers: $1 + 1 = 2$; $5 + 8 = 13$; $89 + 144 = 233$.

Fibonacci numbers in mathematics

This infinitely long series of number has many curious features and follows intriguing mathematical patterns. For example every third number is divisible by two, every fourth number is divisible by three and every fifth number is divisible by five. The sequence is so pervasive that every positive integer (whole number) can be written as the sum of Fibonacci numbers. It is full of an endless number of quirks, some harder to spot than others, such as the 11th Fibonacci number, which is 89, and $1/89 = 0.011235$.

Since Fibonacci's time, mathematicians have found this series strangely intriguing. It turns up, for instance, in Pascal's triangle. Pascal had no idea of using Fibonacci numbers – and yet they turn up in every diagonal in the triangle. They turn up unexpectedly, too, in Mandelbrot sets, the fractal pictures in which every part is made of ever smaller parts of itself. The sequence precisely matches Fibonacci's.

It also appears in logarithmic sequences, prime number multiplication sequences, in binary maths and programming algorithms. Its prevalence is clearly not a satisfying coincidence; it is something so fundamental that mathematicians have been drawn back to it again and again.

13X13

21X21

8X8

5X5

Fibonacci spiral

Not surprisingly, since the sequence was noticed by Fibonacci when studying the growth of rabbit populations, the sequence pops-up in other studies of population growth, and model population dynamics – even enabling the prediction of the growth of urban areas. Less expectedly, they turn up in economic growth models.

Fibonacci numbers often turn up in nature as plants grow: for example, in the number of leaves in one spiral round the stem of a plant, and the number of petals.

Of course, it is clear that Fibonacci numbers are a reflection of the way things grow. Just as Fibonacci recognized, things rarely grow by doubling. Growth involves one thing building on another, and the Fibonacci series mirrors this with perfect clarity. So wherever there is growth of any kind, the chances are the Fibonacci sequence will be in there.

The 'golden ratio'

The Fibonacci series has long held an important position in art and architecture, with the 'golden ratio' connecting the numbers in the sequence. Divide any large Fibonacci number by the preceding number, and the answer is close to the 'golden ratio', 1.618. Thus 8/5 = 1.6; 13/8 = 1.625; 21/13 = 1.615. The higher the numbers you start with, the closer you get to 1.618. The golden ratio, also called the 'golden section' or the 'golden mean', is defined by the equation $(a + b)/a = a/b$. It can be seen in the lengths of the sides of the rectangle $(a + b)/a$.

These proportions are thought to be especially pleasing, and have been used by architects from the ancient Greeks to Le Corbusier, and by artists from Leonardo da Vinci to Salvador Dali.

DO NUMBERS HAVE TO BE REAL?

CONCLUSION:

Bombelli proved that
imaginary numbers are real.

THE SQUARE ROOT OF -1

Numbers are numbers, surely? How can they be imaginary?
Well, some numbers are and these imaginary numbers were
first highlighted more than four centuries ago by Italian
mathematician Rafael Bombelli.

How can a number be imaginary?

It all hinges on the idea of square roots and negatives. A
square root is a number that, when multiplied by itself, gives
the original number. So the square root of 9 is 3 ($3 \times 3 = 9$),
the square root of 4 is 2 ($2 \times 2 = 4$) and the square root of 1 is
1 ($1 \times 1 = 1$) and so on. But what about the roots of negative
numbers? Here there's a problem, because when you multiply
two negative numbers together, you get a positive: $-2 \times -2 = +4$,
and $-1 \times -1 = +1$. So the root of a negative number must exist yet
can't; it is both real and imaginary.

The ancient Egyptians spotted this ambiguity long ago, and
nearly 2,000 years ago the Greek thinker Hero of Alexandria,
who also created an early steam-powered device called the
aeolipile, had his own baffling encounter. He was trying to
work out the volume of a pyramid with its top lopped off and
needed to find the square root of $81 - 144$. The answer is, of
course, $\sqrt{-63}$. But there's no clear answer to this. So Hero
simply switched the sign to a plus and said the answer
was $\sqrt{63}$. It was, of course, a fudge, but what else could
he do? Even negative numbers were regarded warily
in his time, so square roots of negatives were just
not on.

Renaissance maths battles

But the dilemma bubbled up again in sixteenth century as Italian mathematicians competed to solve cubic equations, equations with the form $ax^3 + bx^2 + cx + d = 0$. They were deemed impossible to solve, because they involved finding roots of negative numbers. Of course, in the hothouse world of Italian renaissance maths, solving this conundrum was the ultimate prize. Then in 1535, there was a breakthrough in a bitter showdown between maths heavies Nicolas Fontana 'Tartaglia' (the Stammerer) and Scipione del Ferro (or at least del Ferro's assistant, Fior) in a church in which each of the combatants showed off their solutions. With his more thorough arguments, Tartaglia won this first bout and the coveted Bologna University maths competition, even though del Ferro had actually got there first.

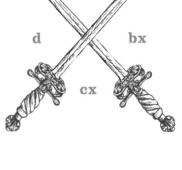

But then 10 years on, the brilliant gambler Girolamo Cardano got hold of del Ferro's notes and waded into the battle with a key book, *Ars Magna*, in which he argued that the root of -1 was possible, though he considered it utterly useless. Armed with Cardano's neat way of solving cubic equations, Cardano's clever young student, Lodovico Ferrari, challenged Tartaglia to another mathematical duel. This time, Tartaglia retired ignominiously, knowing he was beaten.

In each of these duels, the solution involved imaginary numbers. But they were deemed a sleight of hand, rather than actual quantities.

Bombelli enters the fray

This is when Bombelli enters the picture. In 1572 Bombelli wrote a wonderful book called, simply, *Algebra,* in which he explains everything in plain terms the layman can understand.

In it, he set out the issue of imaginary numbers, and complex numbers, which are combinations of real and imaginary numbers, with groundbreaking clarity.

He demonstrated that multiplying two imaginary numbers always gave a real number, and showed how square roots of minus numbers can be used. He called the square root of minus one 'plus of minus' and minus the square root of minus one as 'minus of minus', and gave beautifully simple rules for using imaginary numbers:

Plus of minus times plus of minus makes minus:
$$[+\sqrt{-n} \times +\sqrt{-n} = -n]$$
Plus of minus times minus of minus makes plus:
$$[+\sqrt{-n} \times -\sqrt{-n} = +n]$$
Minus of minus times plus of minus makes plus:
$$[-\sqrt{-n} \times +\sqrt{-n} = +n]$$
Minus of minus times minus of minus makes minus:
$$[-\sqrt{-n} \times -\sqrt{-n} = -n]$$

He, too, at first thought this was trickery. 'The whole matter seemed to rest on sophistry rather than truth,' he wrote. 'Yet I sought so long, until I actually proved this [real result] to be the case.'

The imaginary i

Over the next two centuries, some mathematicians accepted roots of negatives, while others utterly rejected them. In the end, it was Swiss mathematician Leonhard Euler (1707–1783) who saw a way through the dilemma. He introduced the 'imaginary unit', the symbol 'i' for the imaginary number that, when squared, gives -1. So i can also be written $\sqrt{-1}$. Euler's insight meant the square root of any negative number could be included in equations simply as i times the square root of the number. He went on to say that the roots of all negative numbers $\sqrt{-1}$, $\sqrt{-2}$, $\sqrt{-3}$ and so on are imaginary numbers, but 'imaginary' doesn't mean they don't exist; it's simply a mathematical term.

There may be a mystery at the heart of imaginary numbers, and the square root of -1, but it doesn't mean we cannot use it. Indeed, we'd find it hard to live without imaginary numbers nowadays. They're vital for cutting-edge quantum science, but they're also vital in the design of aircraft wings and suspension bridges. They're imaginary because they cannot be tagged to any real number, yet they are 'real' because they are part of the real world. So they are paradoxically both imaginary and real, impossible yet possible. Bombelli certainly started something!

HOW DO YOU ADD WITH BONES?

THE FIRST SIMPLIFICATION OF MULTIPLICATION

1614

ASSOCIATED MATHEMATICIAN:
John Napier

CONCLUSION:
The invention of logarithms, calculators and slide rules.

John Napier was born in 1550 in Merchiston Castle, which is now part of Edinburgh Napier University's Merchiston campus. In 1571, after the death of his father, Napier became the eigth Laird (Baron) of Merchiston.

The sooty cockerel

An enthusiastic inventor, especially of military equipment, he was known as the 'Marvellous Merchiston'. Locals said that he could tell the future, and he kept a black cockerel that was supposed to detect their secret doings. Once, when some valuables were stolen from the castle, Napier ordered his servants into a darkened room in the tower, where they each had to stroke the cockerel, which would crow when touched by the guilty party. But the cock remained silent as they all took their turns, so Napier took them into a lighted room and asked them to hold up their hands. All but one had black hands. The clean-handed servant was accused of theft; he hadn't dared touch the cockerel. Napier had found the thief by the simple act of covering the bird in soot.

Logarithms

Napier was also a keen and enthusiastic physicist and astronomer, and like all scientists at the time, spent much of his time doing tedious calculations, which slowed the process considerably. Around 1590 he discovered a way to simplify

calculations, using what came to be called logarithms, or 'logs' for short. He spent more than 20 years working out logs of numbers, and in 1614 he published his discovery in a book with the snappy title *Mirifici Logarithmorum Canonis Descriptio* (*Describing the Magnificent Logarithms*).

Napier's logs were similar to what today are called 'natural logarithms', written as ln (x) or $\log^e$ (x). The natural log of a number is the power to which the constant, e, has to be raised to equal the number:

ln (x) = a

such that

e^a = x

Thus ln (2.74) = 1.0080 means that $e^{2.74}$ = 2.74, and ln (3.28) = 1.1878 means that $e^{3.28}$ = 3.28. These values could be looked up from a logarithm table.

Why is this useful? Suppose you want to multiply 2.74 × 3.28. Today you would simply use a calculator function, but these things did not exist in the seventeenth century; so they had to do long multiplication. With logs, all you have to do is add the logs:

1.0080 + 1.1878 = 2.1958

Then look up 2.1958 in the logarithm table. It is the log of 8.9872, so this is the answer.

In other words, if you use logs, you do not have to multiply; you can simply add.

The English mathematician Henry Briggs was so astonished and delighted by these logs that he travelled up north to visit Napier. When they met, according to legend, they spent 15 minutes lost in silence and mutual admiration, before Briggs said, 'My Lord. I have undertaken this long journey... to see by what wit or ingenuity you came first to think of this most excellent help unto astronomy, viz the logarithms.'

In due course Briggs converted Napier's logs to base 10, which is what schoolchildren used for centuries to follow.

Napier's bones
Napier went on to invent the first practical pocket calculator, which came to be called Napier's Rods, or, more popularly,

Napier's Bones. He described them in his book *Rabdologia*, published in 1617, shortly before he died.

The bones are really the times tables written down on flat sticks, using Arab lattice multiplication as explained by Fibonacci in his book *Liber Abaci* (see page 57). They are clever, and simple to use. Each column is in practice the multiplication table of that number.

The bones were massively popular for over a century. When the London diarist Samuel Pepys learned arithmetic in 1667 at the age of 29, he wrote, 'To my chamber whither comes Jonas Moore' – his tutor – 'and tells me the mighty use of Napier's Bones.'

The slide rule

The next step forward from Napier's logs was the invention of the slide rule by the Reverend William Oughtred around 1622. The slide rule has logarithmic scales of numbers, which allows multiplication simply by adding, and can also be used for division and trigonometric and other functions. The slide rule became the standard calculating tool for engineers and scientists for several hundred years.

1615

ASSOCIATED MATHEMATICIAN:

Johannes Kepler

HOW BIG IS A BARREL?

MEASURING VOLUME IN SLICES

CONCLUSION:

Kepler used infinitely small slices to calculate the volume of a barrel and make sure he got value for money.

Astronomer Johannes Kepler is best known for his discovery in 1609 of the ellipse shape of the planets' orbits and his three laws of planetary motion. But he also made crucial contributions to mathematics – in particular in the calculation of the area and volume of more complex shapes.

The volume of solids

Calculating the volume of a cube or a pyramid is straightforward. But in 1615, Kepler devised an ingenious way of working out the volumes of other solids and finding their *maxima* (maximum volumes).

His breakthrough emerged as he came to the end of a rather turbulent period in his life. Since 1601, Kepler had been imperial mathematician to Holy Roman Emperor Rudolf II, a job that basically meant casting horoscopes for the court. But in 1612, the empire entered a period of political turbulence as Rudolf died, and Kepler's job came under threat. That same year, his wife, Barbara, had died from Hungarian spotted fever and one of his little boys had died from smallpox. To cap it all, his mother, Katharina, was put on trial for witchcraft. He moved away from the imperial city of Prague to the quieter Linz, and decided to marry again. He went through lists of possible matches, eventually settling on 24-year-old Susanna Reuttinger. It was their wedding celebrations that gave him the inspiration for his ideas on volume calculations.

Marital mathematics

Always eager to get value for money, and a dutiful groom, Kepler began to wonder if wine merchants in Linz, who used different-shaped barrels from his home in the Rhineland, were giving him a good deal. The barrels were stored on their sides and the merchant measured how much wine was in the barrel simply by sticking a rod in through a hole in the middle. He pushed the rod in diagonally into the bottom corner, then checked how far up it was wetted by wine. Maybe this worked for the barrels in Linz, but would it be the same for other barrel shapes?

To Kepler, this became an intriguing intellectual puzzle. Over the next two years, he analyzed all the issues, and in 1615, published his analysis in a book: *Nova Stereometria Doliorum Vinariorum* (*New Solid Geometry of Wine Barrels*) – a uniquely intriguing title for a groundbreaking maths book!

First Kepler investigated ways of calculating areas and volumes, especially curved shapes. Mathematicians had long theorized about using 'indivisibles' – elements so tiny they cannot be divided. These can, in theory, be fitted into the shape and added up. You could find the area of a circle, for instance, using slender pie-slice triangles, which is how Archimedes had estimated the value of pi.

And Kepler had already employed the idea when he needed to calculate the area of ellipses for his work on planetary orbits. Instead of the triangles, which Archimedes had used for circles, Kepler, following lead of the fourteenth-century French philosopher Nicole Oresme, divided the ellipse into an infinite number of vertical slices. He could then work out the area of the ellipse using the vertical heights or ordinates of each slice.

Accepting infinitesimals

It was a natural extension for Kepler to look at finding the volume of a barrel or any other solid shape, by imagining it as a stack of thin layers. The total volume then, of course, is the sum of the volumes of the layers. In a barrel, each layer is a very shallow cylinder, and it's easy to calculate the volume of a cylinder. Simple.

But wait – if the cylinders have no thickness, then they've no volume. So how about making thicker slices? Well, no, that won't work because cylinders have straight sides and barrels are curved. Kepler's way out of this conundrum was to accept the idea of 'infinitesimals' – the infinitely thinnest slices that can exist without vanishing altogether. Kepler wasn't the first to think of this by any means, but his work brought the idea to prominence.

Now Kepler had a method of calculating volume, he used the same method to find which shape of barrel gives the maximum volume, and get to the nub of his issue with the merchant's rod. This time he used triangles formed by the cylinders' height, its diameter and a diagonal from top to bottom. Then he was able to ask – if the diagonal is fixed like the merchant's rod, how will changing the height change the volume?

It turned out that short, squat barrels with a height about twice the diameter – like the barrels in Austria – gave the maximum volume. As it happened, the tall barrels from Kepler's homeland on the Rhine held much less wine. Kepler also noticed that the nearer the maximum the shape gets, the less the volume increases.

Groundwork for calculus

This was an observation that also played a key part in the subsequent development of calculus, with its exploration of maxima and minima. Kepler's adoption of infinitesimals was an equally important piece of groundwork for the later development of calculus by Newton and Leibniz. Maths had a problem with nature in that nature isn't broken into neat blocks like numbers and geometric shapes. It's continuous and varied. But infinitesimals turned out to be incredibly useful in bridging the gap and helping maths to play a key part in our modern knowledge of the world.

WHAT ARE CARTESIAN COORDINATES?

THE RISE OF ANALYTICAL GEOMETRY

1637

ASSOCIATED
MATHEMATICIAN:
Descartes

CONCLUSION:
A fly inspired Descartes'
brilliant system of axes
and coordinates.

René Descartes was born in 1596, near Tours in central France. His family was rich, and he was sent to an exclusive Jesuit school at La Flèche, where, because of his poor health, he was not roused at 5 a.m. like the other students, but allowed to stay in bed until 11 a.m., a habit he continued for the rest of his life. He did well at school, but came to the conclusion that the only thing he had learned was how ignorant he was. After spending some time in Paris and joining a couple of armies, he went to Holland for 20 years, working on mathematics and philosophy.

Descartes is remembered primarily for his philosophical ideas, especially his discourse on method. He decided that he could not be sure of anything that he read, or saw, or heard, and that he must go back to first principles. Famously he wrote *Cogito ergo sum* ('I think, therefore I am'). In other words, I am thinking, and therefore there must be somebody doing the thinking, and that somebody is me. Today many philosophers and psychologists reject the idea of a continuous self who does the thinking, as well as 'Cartesian dualism' – the idea that body and mind are made of different substances. Nevertheless, he has been called the father of modern philosophy.

Analytical geometry

Descartes was immensely active in mathematics too, writing a good deal, and collaborating with Pierre de Fermat on various projects. The most important thing he did was to invent coordinates, now known as Cartesian coordinates.

Imagine that you are a pigeon, or a helicopter pilot, and you want to fly from Orford, on the coast

of Suffolk, England, to a destination in the sea, 13 kilometres (8 miles) roughly north-east. How are you going to find it if the weather is foggy?

Satnav won't help much out at sea, and nor will a map, since there are no landmarks to guide you. To find where the target is, what you need are its coordinates.

You can see that the target is 12 kilometres (7.5 miles) east of Orford, and 5 kilometres (3.1 miles) north. In other words, its coordinates are (12, 5). Knowing that, you can either fly 12 kilometres east and then 5 kilometres north, or you can calculate the correct compass bearing, which is about 22.5 degrees, and fly 13 kilometres direct.

Descartes hit on the idea of using algebra to describe geometry. He pioneered the use of x, y, and z as unknowns, and a, b, and c as knowns in equations such as $ax^2 + by^2 = c$. He was the first to show x squared as x^2 and y cubed as y^3. Allegedly he dreamed all this up in a flash of inspiration while lying in bed one morning in Holland, watching a fly on his ceiling.

Cartesian coordinates

In analytic geometry, every point on the flat surface has a pair of real-number coordinates. The points shown in this diagram are (3, 4), (7, –1.5) and (12, 5). East is replaced by +x, and north by +y; negative coordinates work perfectly well.

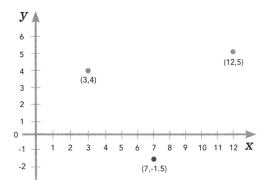

These coordinates allow you to make pictures of equations. For example, if $y = (x/2) - 2$, then when x = 0, y = –2; when x = 4, y = 0; and when x = 10, y = 3. The graph of the equation is a straight line through these points.

Cartesian coordinates work in three dimensions, too. Points in this 'Euclidian space' are located by three variables, x, y, and z.

The power of the Cartesian coordinate system is that it allows problems in geometry to be turned into problems about numbers, and vice versa. It also allows you to describe curves algebraically and to calculate, using algebra, distances, angles between straight lines, areas, and points at which curves intersect.

There are other useful coordinate systems, of which the best-known is the polar coordinate system. Here, a point on the surface is located by the distance from the origin (the pole), r (for radius), and the angle with the x axis, θ (theta). The point is expressed as a distance and direction from the origin. This system has a great deal of uses, particularly in physics, where it is used for mapping orbital motion.

The spherical coordinate system uses polar coordinates in three dimensions. There are also coordinate systems with narrow, specific uses, such as canonical coordinates, which are used in Hamiltonian classical mechanics. Yet, none of these have come close to replacing Cartesian coordinates. It is a system that is easy to remember and easy to teach children.

Cartesian coordinates

1653

ASSOCIATED
MATHEMATICIAN:

Blaise Pascal

CONCLUSION:
Winning in a game of
chance can be calculated.

WHAT ARE THE CHANCES?

THE INVENTION OF PROBABILITY THEORY

Antoine Gombaud, the self-styled Chevalier de Méré, was one
of the stars of the French salon in the mid-1600s. Witty and
urbane, he was a liberal thinker who revelled in the company of
intelligent people. He was also a gambler and became intrigued
by the problem of how to divide stakes fairly if a game of chance
was suddenly broken off. A game might normally end only when
one player had won a certain number of rounds, for instance.
But if it were cut short, how should the stakes be split to reflect
the number of rounds each player had actually won?

A flawed field

Gombaud knew some seriously top-class maths brains in the
salon of Marin Mersenne and threw this challenge open to
the Mersenne salon in 1652. Two men took it up: the brilliant
French philosopher mathematician Blaise Pascal, (1623–1662)
and the equally brilliant Pierre de Fermat (1607–1665). What
Gombaud could never have anticipated was just what profound
answers these maths giants would come up with. Together, in a
series of letters, they laid the foundations of probability theory.

Gambling had already spurred some insight into the issue.
In the previous century Italian mathematicians such as
Pacioli, Cardano and Tartaglia (the Stammerer) had come up
with ideas about the chances of dice giving certain numbers
or hands of cards coming out a particular way. But their
understanding was at best vague and at worst plain wrong.
The work of Fermat, and more significantly, Pascal, was of a
different order.

Over the next year, Pascal worked at the problem diligently.
He saw that the probability of any event is the proportion of
times it will happen. A dice has six faces, so the chances it will

land on any particular face when rolled, are 1 in 6, or 1/6. In other words, finding the probability means noting how many ways the event can occur, and dividing it by the total number of possibilities.

Pascal's triangle

A calculation like this is simple for a single dice but if you're rolling two dice, or dealing 52 playing cards, the calculations become mind-bogglingly complex. Just how many possible combinations of six cards are there, for instance?

As Pascal realized, the answers lie in binomials – expressions with two terms: say, x + y. In this case, one of the terms is the number of possible combinations, and the other is the total number of objects (say, cards or dice). The probabilities emerge by multiplying the binomial the desired number of times, n: $(x + y)^n$. Multiplying a binomial by a given power gives a pattern of coefficients: the numbers that appear in front of the term. So $(x + y)^2$ gives $1x^2 + 2xy + 1y^2$; $(x + y)^3$ gives $1x^3 + 3x^2y + 3xy^2 + 1y^3$; and so on, with the coefficients in italics.

This all still sounds complex, but as he worked on the problem, Pascal had a stroke of genius. He decided to set out the possible outcomes, step by step methodically, in rows representing the rounds played. As the rounds progressed, there was an ever-widening range of possible outcomes, so the steps created an equilateral triangle built from a simple arrangement of numbers. Each number is the sum of the two adjacent numbers in the row above.

The numbers in the triangle match the number of possible combinations when you choose a particular

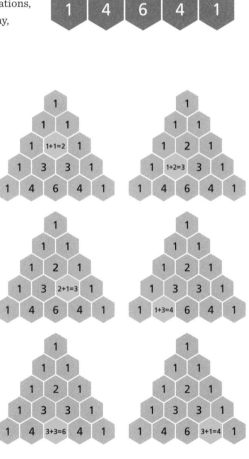

number of objects from a particular number of options. Amazingly, each row in the triangle gives the binomial coefficients for a particular power: 1,2,1; 1,3,3,1. This means you have to look in the right row to find the range of probabilities. Pascal only showed a triangle of limited size, but there is no reason it can't stretch into infinity. The correspondence between binomial coefficients and the numbers in the triangle is not a coincidence. It reveals a fundamental truth about numbers and probability, and this discovery laid the foundation of probability theory.

It turns out that this triangle, now known as Pascal's triangle, has some truly remarkable qualities beyond simply being a look-up for binomials. It is, in fact, much older than Pascal; as long ago as 450 BCE it appears in Indian texts as the 'Staircase of Mount Meru'. But it was Pascal who really set the ball rolling.

More than gambling

Over the centuries since, mathematicians have discovered many significant patterns in the triangle. One of the most interesting is the Fibonacci sequence (see page 57). And adding the numbers above each row gives you a Mersenne number – that is, a prime number that is one less than a power of two, such as 2, 3, 5, 7, 13, 17, 19, 31.

Even more remarkably, you get beautiful fractal patterns when you colour in numbers divisible. And colouring all numbers divisible by two creates an astonishing pattern of triangles called Sierpinski triangles, after the Polish mathematician Waclaw Sierpinski (1885–1969). The triangle really seems to be a gold mine, or an iceberg, for mathematicians, revealing more secrets as they dive deeper.

Sierpinski triangles

CAN YOU CALCULATE SPEED IN TINY STEPS?

THE INVENTION OF CALCULUS

1665

ASSOCIATED
MATHEMATICIANS:
Isaac Newton
Gotfried Leibniz

CONCLUSION:
Calculus can be used
to work out the rate of
change in an infinitely
short time.

Isaac Newton was a sickly lad. When he was born, on
Christmas Eve 1642, he was so small and feeble that they
did not expect him to last the night. His father died before he
was born, and when he was two, his mother married a rich
clergyman, leaving him in the not-too-tender care of her
parents. He grew up lonely and introspective, but acquired a
remarkable ability for focusing on a range of problems, which
made him perhaps the greatest scientist of all time.

Working through the plague

Newton's headmaster managed to get him into Cambridge
to study law, but in 1665 the plague arrived, Cambridge was
closed down, and Newton went back to his mother's house in
Woolsthorpe, near Grantham.

There, at home alone, he worked on a series of challenges,
from the colours of the rainbow to the orbits of the Moon and
the planets, and in pure mathematics he invented calculus.
As he himself wrote, some 50 years later, 'All this was in the
two plague years 1665 and 1666, for in those days I was in the
prime of my age for invention, and minded mathematics and
philosophy more than at any time since.'

Today calculus is used all the time by engineers, scientists,
medical researchers, computer scientists and economists,
but Newton invented it to solve a problem left by Italian
scientist Galileo Galilei.

Galileo's balls

In the 1590s, Galileo studied the science of falling. Aristotle
had asserted that big things fall faster than little ones:
that a brick would fall twice as fast as a half brick. Galileo

disagreed, and allegedly dropped balls of various weights off the Leaning Tower of Pisa to show that they all fell at the same speed.

He went on to carry out a more scientific experiment, using a slope. He cut a groove along a wooden beam, polished it, and lined it with parchment. Then he propped up one end of it and allowed a polished bronze ball to roll down from the top. By using this inclined plane (in effect slowing down the fall), he was able to make careful measurements of how fast it descended.

The ball went faster and faster as it rolled down, and Galileo showed that it would roll one unit of distance in one second, four units in two seconds, nine units in three seconds, and 16 units in four seconds. The distance rolled was proportional to the square of the time.

He realized that the ball was accelerating at a constant rate, or as he put it, 'when starting from rest, acquires during equal time intervals equal increments of velocity'. He was unable to describe the motion mathematically, however, but Newton picked up the story some 70 years later.

Newton's method of fluxions

Newton realized that to calculate the velocity of Galileo's ball at any moment, he needed to work out the instantaneous rate of change of position. Suppose d was the distance rolled and t the time, and suppose the time increases by a small quantity q. Since the distance is proportional to the square of the time, the extra distance rolled will be $(t + q)^2 - t^2$, which is equal to $(2tq + q^2)$.

While t increases to $(t + q)$, the average rate of change (which Newton called the *fluxion* of *d*) is $(2tq + q^2) \div q$, or $(2t + q)$. But q is only a small quantity, and if it shrinks, the rate of change $(2t + q)$ gets closer and closer to $2t$. In the limit, as q approaches zero, the rate of change becomes equal to $2t$.

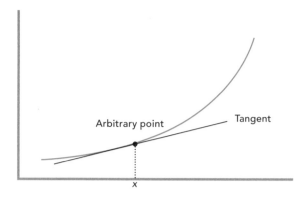

This is called differentiating, and the process is differential calculus. We would now say that the differential of t^2 is 2t.

This does not sound complicated, but it was a giant leap forward, because what Newton was actually doing was looking at an infinitely small period of time. Tackling infinities was extremely tricky, but it changed maths forever.

One thing this calculus allows you to do is calculate the slope of a curve. Suppose this curve is the graph of t^2, then we can find the slope of the curve - the tangent - at any point.

Newton's book *Method of Luxions* was completed in 1671, but not published until 1736, long after his death. This delay was partly because Newton was secretive, and did not want anyone to criticize or steal his ideas. He used the methods of calculus to solve the problem of planetary motion, the surface of a rotating fluid, the shape of the earth, and many other problems discussed in his 1687 masterwork, *Principia Mathematica*.

The Leibniz row

Meanwhile, German mathematician Gottfried Wilhelm Leibniz invented calculus quite independently (about 1673), seven years after Newton, but published straight away. Soon a furious row broke out, both men accusing the other of stealing their results. Because Leibniz published first, however, and used clearer notation, his system is what came to be used everywhere.

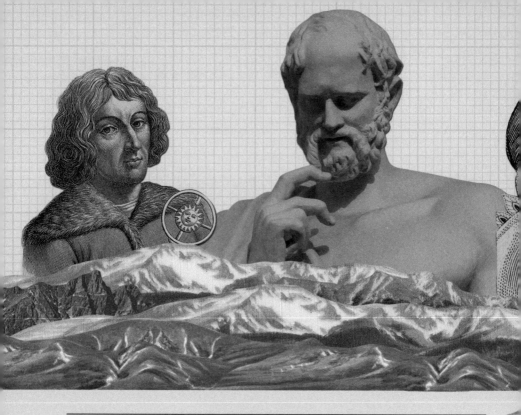

CHAPTER 4: Bridging the space between maths: 1666 – 1796

Isaac Newton famously said, 'If I have seen further, it is by standing on the shoulders of giants.' The same, too, can be said about the mathematical discoveries that followed from his (and Leibniz's) invention of calculus. They had given mathematicians a new tool to figure out the secrets of the universe. And said mathematicians took the opportunities this presented with both hands, with two of them towering above the rest.

The period after Newton was the age of Euler, which was followed by the emergence of one of the few figures whose all-round brilliance come close to Euler's, Carl Gauss. They were undoubtedly two of the greatest mathematicians who ever lived, both contributing to fields as diverse as classical mechanics and number theory. There were other brilliant mathematicians around at this time, notably Lagrange and the Bernoullis, but Euler and Gauss were two giants of the post-Newtonian age.

1728

ASSOCIATED MATHEMATICIAN:
Leonhard Euler

WHAT WAS EULER'S NUMBER?

CONCLUSION:
Euler's number, *e*, is the constant of continuous growth.

THE NUMBER BEHIND ALL GROWTH

Things grow all the time. Bacteria multiply. Populations grow. Fires spread. Species invade. Compound interest escalates. The maths of all these and more comes into calculus, which is about rates of change. And in calculus, there is one number that matters more than any other: Euler's number, or Euler's constant, *e*. If you're doing calculations about growth or rates of change, you want *e*.

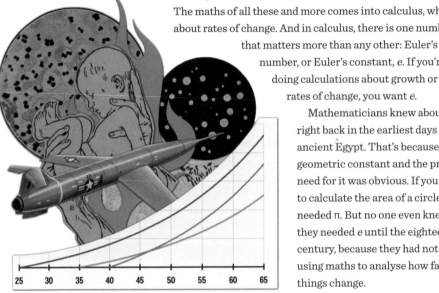

Mathematicians knew about π right back in the earliest days of ancient Egypt. That's because it is a geometric constant and the practical need for it was obvious. If you wanted to calculate the area of a circle, you needed π. But no one even knew they needed *e* until the eighteenth century, because they had not started using maths to analyse how fast things change.

Logarithm tables

The constant had started to appear in the seventeenth century as mathematicians began to develop logarithms. In Napier's book of logarithms, there's an appendix giving the natural logarithms of various numbers. Logarithms are the numbers of growth, and natural logarithms are logarithms that use *e* as a base rather than 10 as in common logarithms, but Napier did not use the term *e*, and its significance wasn't appreciated. Later in the century, the brilliant Dutch scientist Christiaan Huygens identified the 'logarithmic' curve on a graph.

Huygens's logarithmic curve is the curve we would today identify as an exponential curve, and is the curve that *e* unlocks. Exponential growth is sometimes wrongly taken to mean just superfast and accelerating. But it has a very specific meaning. It means the growth is proportional to the quantity at any one time. So if a population of rabbits doubles every month, we would have two, then four, then eight, 16, 32, 64, 128, 256, and so on.

Growing interest

The significance of *e* emerged in 1683, when the Swiss mathematician Johann Bernoulli began to calculate compound interest. If you had a bank generous enough to give you 100% interest on your £1 deposit every year, at the end of the year you'd have £2. But what if the bank offers you 50% every 6 months? After the first six months, you'd have £1.50, and after the year, you'd have gained 50% interest on £1.50, so you'd have £2.25.

In fact, the more frequently you calculate interest, the more interest you gain by compounding. But as you calculate ever more frequently, the gains diminish. By the time you're calculating it every day, you'd be earning £2.71, and that's getting very close to the limit, with the gains diminishing more and more if you divide into minutes, then seconds. So what would you get if you calculated interest every instant? This would be the very maximum, and at this point growth levels out entirely.

E has it

Bernoulli knew this figure must be between two and three, but he could not work it out exactly, and he had no idea of the link with logarithms. This is where Leonhard Euler comes in. In a letter to Christian Goldbach in 1731, he calls this number *e*. It's nice that '*e*' is the initial letter of his name, and also the first letter of 'exponential', but Euler probably named it '*e*' because it's the first vowel after 'a.'

Much more important than the naming of *e*, which subsequently became known as Euler's number, was his calculation of a value of it. He published it in 1748 in *Introductio in Analysin Infinitorum (Introduction to Analysis*

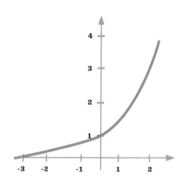

The curve y=e^x

of the Infinite). He worked out the number using factorials. Two factorial is written 2! which means $1 \times 2 = 2$; 3 factorial, or 3!, which means $1 \times 2 \times 3 = 6$, and so on. In other words, to get any factorial, you multiply together all the numbers from 1 up to that number. But with *e*, the factorials are, of course, fractions, since we're talking about diminishing divisions.

$e = 1 + 1/1! + 1/2! + 1/3!...$ Or $2 + 1/2 + 1/6 = 2.666...$
$e = 1 + 1/1! + 1/2! + 1/3! + 1/4!$ Or $2 + 1/2 + 1/6 + 1/24 = 2.708333...$

Euler needed to calculate them all the way up to infinity. He gave a figure up to 18 decimal places:
$e = 2.718281828459045235$
He didn't explain where he got it, but he probably only needed to go to 1/20! In 1962, Donald Knuth calculated *e* to 1,271 decimal places, but mathematicians haven't felt the same need to nail *e* precisely as with π, and for most purposes Euler's figure is quite enough.

The growth constant
What makes *e* special is that it's the growth constant. With a graph showing the growth of y in terms of powers of *e*, e^x then at any point the value of y is e^x, the gradient is e^x and the area under the curve is also e^x. That means you can get one from any of the others and this is amazingly useful. In fact, most modern calculus would be hugely more difficult without it.

Euler also came up with another key maths symbol, *i*, which stands for the square root of -1. He was able to unite them in what some mathematicians regard as the most simple and beautiful formula ever devised.

$e^{i\pi} + 1 = 0$

Many say this formula sums up all of maths.

CAN YOU CROSS THE BRIDGES?

THE GAME THAT GAVE US GRAPH THEORY

1736

ASSOCIATED
MATHEMATICIANS:
Leonhard Euler

CONCLUSION:
Graph theory is the branch of mathematics that studies connections.

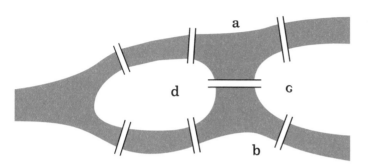

River
Pregel

According to legend, the inhabitants of Königsberg in Prussia (now Kaliningrad, Russia) used to spend their summer evenings walking along and across the River Pregel, and enjoyed crossing the river on seven bridges. There are two islands in the river, and the bridges link them with the mainland. A local challenge was to cross every bridge once and only once, but nobody could achieve it. Was this because of the wine in the cafés, or because of the geometry?

Suppose, for example, that you start in the north-west corner, and cross bridge 1 to the island, then 2 to get back to the mainland. Next, cross 4 to get to the other island, 3 to get back to the first island, 6 and 5 to get back to the island – but then you are stuck on the island, and you have not crossed bridge 7.

If there were only bridges 1, 5, 6 and 2, or bridges 1, 5, 7, 4, it would be easy, but these seven bridges pose a serious puzzle. The islands seem to make it more difficult. At first sight you might think you need an even number of bridges, but you could easily get back to base by crossing five: 1, 5, 6, 3, and 4. The inhabitant strollers must have become seriously confused.

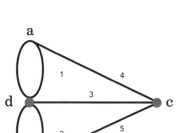

a

d

c

b

1

2

3

4

5

Graph theory

The puzzle was solved by Swiss mathematical genius Leonhard Euler, who pointed out that the route across the land was irrelevant; the only thing that mattered was the pattern of the bridges. He showed what he meant by reducing the puzzle to a graph, where the green parts (he called them nodes) represent the land and the black lines are the bridges.

Euler solved the problem by proving convincingly that there is no way to cross the bridges without repetition. Indeed, he created a method showing situations in which there was a route – but that Köninsgberg was not among them.

What matters is not layout or geometry of the routes but simply the pattern of the turning points. Euler reduced the entire problem to a pattern of dots representing each piece of land, and lines connecting the points or 'nodes.'

Universal network

This is how he created a universal method. Following Euler, you can examine any similar problem simply by reducing it to lines and nodes. The lines do not need to bear any relation to reality, nor do the nodes; it is entirely graphical. All you need is the nodes in roughly the right places, and lines connecting them.

This simple idea not only turned a geographical problem into a mathematical one, it also inspired many mapmakers who realized that they only often needed to show graphically the connections between places, not the intricate detail of the winding roads between. You only have to look at maps of airline routes, or the classic map of the London underground to realize how powerful and pervasive this idea is.

Good connections

So he got just four dots for the land masses, and seven lines for the seven bridges. What this shows instantly is how well-connected each node is. Three of them have three connections, and one, the central-island node, has five. This idea of how many connections a node has is now called 'valency' and it's crucial in topology, the vast field of maths Euler's work on the Königsberg bridges inspired.

Euler looked at closed tours, where the tour returns to the same point, and open tours where it ends up at a different point. It is immediately intuitively obvious that if all the nodes have odd numbers of connections, a route cannot be found. You've got to have the same number of points for leaving as arriving. In other words, you have to have at least one node with an even number of connections.

The same is true for an open tour. However you arrange it, there must be just two nodes exactly with an even number of connections, one for the start of and one for the end.

Euler went on to prove that this must be so mathematically, turning the number of connections into numbers. His proof was quite complex, but today it can be done much more simply.

Where to now?

Euler's solution - or rather proof that there is no solution - was an ingenious piece of deduction. His method of reducing the problem to lines and nodes in order to be able to treat it mathematically developed in a way that even he couldn't have foreseen.

First of all, it provided a terrific new way for mathematicians to solve problems like this, and the range of problems it could be applied to mushroomed. Today it's used for planning the movement of goods, for instance. But then mathematicians began to realize there is a whole mathematical world to explore with networks, surfaces and layouts. This world is called topology, and it really came into its own in the early twentieth century as scientists and mathematicians began to explore multidimensional space, and mathematicians began to realize it provided a route for solving complex equations. It is still on the very cutting edge of high-level maths, as the recent work of the late Maryam Mirzakhani shows. Euler's bridges reached a long way!

DO EVEN NUMBERS
DIVIDE INTO PRIMES?

CONCLUSION:
Goldbach's famous
conjecture on primes has
yet to be solved.

A FRUSTRATINGLY SIMPLE THEOREM

For mathematicians in the seventeenth and eighteenth
centuries, the idea of numbers, or rather integers, held an
extraordinary fascination. It was purely intellectual curiosity.
It served no apparent practical purpose whatsoever. And
yet some of the most brilliant minds of the age devoted their
attention to what were, in many ways, games with numbers.
Number theory, as it came to be called, was for them the
purest form of intellectual activity: a great puzzle that could be
pursued in one's own study with nothing but a pen and paper.

One of these number puzzlers was Christian Goldbach.
He was clever, though not especially brilliant, but came up
with one simple yet remarkable proposition. Known as
the Goldbach conjecture, it has turned out to be
beyond any mathematician since either to prove
or disprove. It is one of the oldest unsolved
problems in mathematics.

The centre of the mathematical world

Goldbach was born in Königsberg in
1690. Königsberg was a small Prussian
city, now Kaliningrad in Russia, and yet
there was something special going on there
intellectually in the eighteenth century. It was
home to a remarkable cluster of great minds,
including the brilliant philosopher Immanuel
Kant and, perhaps more importantly, the pre-eminent
mathematician of the day and the doyen of number theory,
Leonhard Euler.

At the age of 35, Goldbach became professor of mathematics
and historian of the Imperial Academy at St Petersburg, and he

was clearly good at making connections with the Russian court. Three years later he went to Moscow as tutor to Tsar Peter II, and from 1742 he served as a staff member of the Russian Ministry of Foreign Affairs. And it was at this time, now 52 years old, that he came up with the first inklings of the idea that was to make his name famous among mathematicians.

The Goldbach conjecture

On 7 June 1742, Goldbach wrote an excited letter to Euler. In it, he described a remarkable discovery he had just made about prime numbers - or so he thought. A prime number is a number that can be divided by no other number but 1. Goldbach wrote:

Every integer, which can be written as the sum of two primes, can also be written as the sum of as many primes as one wishes, until all terms are units.

In other words, every number from two upwards can be made by adding together just a few prime numbers.

Euler was excited by the idea, and the two mathematicians corresponded several times over it. Euler crucially turned Goldbach's statement the other way round. Now it said that every even number could be split into two primes:

$6 = 3 + 3$

$8 = 3 + 5$

$10 = 3 + 7 = 5 + 5$

$12 = 7 + 5$

...

$100 = 3 + 97 = 11 + 89 = 17 + 83 = 29 + 71 = 41 + 59 = 47 + 53$

And so on, up to infinity. This was a big and simple claim. In a letter dated 30 June 1742, the brilliant Euler expressed his conviction that Goldbach was right and yet he could not prove it. And neither has any mathematician since.

Attempts to prove the Goldbach conjecture

As the correspondence between the two Königsbergers continued, different permutations of the idea emerged. There are now considered two key versions of Goldbach's conjecture:

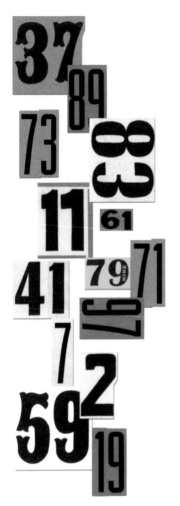

the 'weak' version, and the more comprehensive 'strong' version, which, if proved, must also prove the weak version. The weak version, essentially Goldbach's original, says any odd number is the sum of no more than three primes. The strong version, which is pretty much how Euler stated it, is that even numbers are the sum of just two primes.

Goldbach's conjecture is such a simple idea that it has nagged at mathematicians ever since. It seems so simple that they believe that unlocking the puzzle must somehow reveal some fundamental truth about numbers.

One approach has been to find a number that does not conform. If even a single exception is found, the conjecture fails. In 2013 a computer ran every even number up to 4×10^{18} (4,000,000,000,000,000,000) and no exception was generated. The bigger the number, the more possible primes you can combine to create it, so it seems highly unlikely that we will ever find an exception.

But for mathematicians, 'highly unlikely' is not proof, therefore, many since have looked for mathematical proofs. The result is that several variations of the conjecture have actually been proved. In 1930, for instance, Soviet mathematician Lev Shnirelman showed that every number can be made from no more than 20 primes. In 1937, another Soviet mathematician, Ivan Vinogradov, proved that every large odd number can be made from just three primes.

The continuing draw of this enigma is such that in 2000, publishers Faber & Faber went so far as to offer $1 million for anyone who could prove the strong conjecture. In 2012, Australian-American Terence Tao came close to proving the weak conjecture, by confirming that odd numbers can be made from at most five primes. But no one has got close with the strong conjecture, which seems destined to defeat even the brightest mathematical minds.

HOW DO YOU CALCULATE FLOW?

RESTRICTING FLOW AND CONSERVING ENERGY

1752

ASSOCIATED
MATHEMATICIAN:
Daniel Bernoulli

CONCLUSION:
Studying the flow of
blood inspired Bernoulli
to explain why speed
decreases as pressure
increases.

The Bernoulli principle, or equation, discovered by Swiss
mathematician Daniel Bernoulli around 1730, is one of the
most fundamental insights into the flow of fluids ever made.
It shows that under particular conditions, pressure and speed
are inversely related. More particularly, as a fluid slows down,
its pressure goes up, and vice versa. It plays a key part in
understanding everything from why wings keep an aircraft
flying to how a baseball pitcher throws a curveball.

Bernoulli was barely 30 years old when he made the
discovery, working in St Petersburg in Russia under the
patronage of Empress Catherine I. His assistant was
another brilliant young Swiss mathematician, Leonhard
Euler, and the two of them became fascinated by the
mathematics of fluid flow.

Flowing through veins and arteries

Bernoulli's interest in fluid flow arose, ironically,
because he had been steered by his
famous mathematician father,
Johann, away from his beloved
maths and into medicine against
his will. As he studied medicine,
Daniel became fascinated by
William Harvey's theory of blood
circulation, developed about a century
earlier. Bernoulli's interest wasn't physiological. He was
intrigued by the way blood flowed through arteries and
veins, and how the blood's pressure and speed might vary.

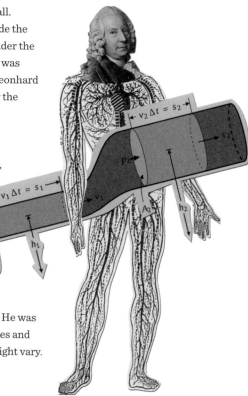

Medicine fell by the wayside, and his interest in the topic led him to invent a ship's hourglass through which the sand would flow steadily even in the stormiest weather. It was this simple invention that won him first prize at the French Academy of Sciences, and earned him his invitation to Russia. But the flow of sand through the neck of the hourglass gave him crucial ideas for understanding how the molecules in a fluid like blood might behave when it flowed through a neck-like restriction.

The conservation of energy

Another crucial insight came from a topic that had caught his imagination as a teenager in mathematical chats with his dad: the conservation of energy – the idea that the total amount of energy in a system never changes, however many transformations it goes through internally. If you sit on a swing, for instance, at the top of your swing, you have lots of 'potential' energy due to your height. As you swing down, you lose potential energy, but you accelerate and gain 'kinetic' energy, the energy of movement, and this carries up the far side.

With Euler, Bernoulli started experimenting with the flow of water through pipes of varying diameters. He noticed that water flows slowly in wide sections, but speeds up as soon as it enters a restriction. Bearing in mind the law of the conservation of energy, the acceleration could not involve any change in energy.

Bernoulli realized that as the fluid passed through the restriction, its kinetic energy must increase with the speed. But where is this extra kinetic energy coming from? As with the swing, it must come from potential energy, and the potential energy must be due to higher pressure in the wider section, which is driving the flow. Unlike a gas, which is squeezed when constricted, water is incompressible, and the situation is rather like the sand running through the hourglass neck.

But the extra speed and energy in the restricted energy can't come without a loss: pressure. As the neck narrows the flow and the speed goes up, the pressure must go down.

To prove it, Bernoulli punctured the wall of the pipe and inserted an open-ended vertical glass straw. The height the fluid rose up the straw gave a clear indication of the pressure. Inserting a thin glass tube into an artery soon became the standard, if rather brutal, way for physicians to measure blood flow and remained so for almost 170 years.

Restricted flow

With this simple device Bernoulli was able to prove that as a fluid enters a restriction, the flow accelerates and the pressure drops. This is called Bernoulli's principle. Twenty or so years later, Euler formulated this principle into an equation now known as Bernoulli's equation:

$$v^2/2 + gz + P/\rho = \text{constant}$$

where v is the fluid flow speed; g is the acceleration due to gravity; z is the height; P is the pressure at the chosen point; and ρ is the density of the fluid at all points in the fluid.

One important restriction was that just as the gas laws are restricted to 'ideal' gases, so Bernoulli's principle only applies to what is called laminar flow. Laminar flow is smooth and regular, and always moves at the same speed and in the same direction. It does not work with turbulent flow, but it works for laminar flows of both liquids and gases.

The key insight of the Bernoulli principle is that squeezing a flow makes it accelerate and reduces its pressure. This comes into play in many situations. It's why, for instance, when air flows over a curved aircraft wing it speeds up, loses pressure and creates lift. The same is true of a curved sail.

Bernoulli took some time to publish his ideas, wary of upsetting his father. Eventually, in 1737, he wrote it all down in a book called *Hydrodynamica*, with a dedication to his dad. But Johann, far from being mollified, retaliated with his own book on the subject, *Hydraulics*, borrowing many of his son's ideas. It was at this point Daniel effectively gave up on maths. The pressure was too much for him simply to go with the flow.

1772

ASSOCIATED
MATHEMATICIANS:

Joseph-Louis Lagrange

WHERE CAN YOU PARK IN SPACE?

CONCLUSION:

There are mathematically identifiable points in space where gravitational pull is perfectly balanced.

THE THREE-BODY PROBLEM

Ever since Newton's delineation of gravity, mathematicians have been fascinated by the three-body problem. By this, of course, they are not talking about a troublesome ménage, but how the mutual gravitational pull of three 'bodies', like planets or moons, works together.

In 1687, with his theory of gravity, Newton had shown how two bodies interact, and how they pull each other together along a line between their centres of gravity. Factor in the momentum of the bodies, which acts in opposition to gravity, and you can calculate how they move with fairly simple maths. But what happens when you add a third body that forms a triangle, such as that between the Sun, the Earth and the Moon?

Complex mechanics

The maths that comes into play when you add this third body is phenomenally complex, and even now, after almost three and half centuries of attention by some of the greatest mathematical minds, the issue is not entirely solved.

Gravitational attraction is mutual. The Sun, Moon and Earth each have their own momentum, but each is influenced by the pull of both the other bodies simultaneously, and this is changing constantly as they dance through space and the distance between them varies. Plus, neither the Earth nor Moon are perfectly round, which adds to the difficulty.

Many mathematicians have tried to get a handle by looking at only a limited aspect of the problem. Most explore the movement of the Moon. But in 1760, Swiss mathematician Leonhard Euler introduced the restricted three-body problem, in which the third body is only an infinitesimally small particle, with no gravitational effect on the other two.

It was this that fascinated Joseph-Louis Lagrange, who took over from Euler as the director of mathematics at the Prussian Academy of Sciences in Berlin. Lagrange was born in Turin, the son of a once-rich French soldier who lost all his money through speculation. Young Lagrange was a prodigy and became a professor at his college at the tender age of 17.

It was in Berlin that Lagrange did his best mathematical work, including his treatise *Mécanique analytique* of 1788, perhaps the greatest work on mathematical physics of the century. In this book, Lagrange developed the 'calculus of variations', completely reformulating the focus of mechanics from directional forces in the Newtonian model to work and energy in his model, known as Lagrangian mechanics. With Newtonian mechanics, you have to know the direction forces are operating in; Lagrange works with energy that is not dependent on direction, which proved to be far more useful for calculating movements of particles then Newton.

Lagrangian mechanics made for both easier calculations and a more profound understanding of how movement in the universe happens. It is an astonishing feat of algebra. Lagrange was a great believer in the power of analytic algebra without resorting to geometry, and categorically refused to have diagrams in his works.

Lagrangian points

En route to the *Mécanique analytique*, Lagrange looked at Euler's restricted three-body problem, which led him to a remarkable discovery, now known as Lagrangian points. Euler had already been working with a version of the problem in which the third body is so tiny it has no gravitational influence on the other two bodies. Lagrange's technique was to restrict the problem still more by making the orbits circular and ignoring the Coriolis force (force created by the rotation of a planet).

Lagrangian points are minute locations in space where the combined gravitational forces of two bodies, such as the Sun and Earth, or the Earth and Moon, exactly balance the centrifugal force felt by a smaller body. This interaction

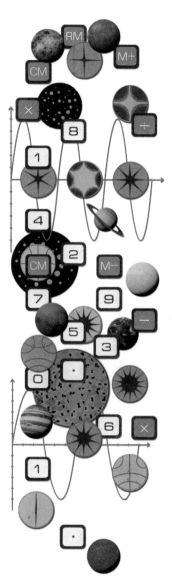

creates a 'parking place' in space where the small body, which could be an asteroid or spacecraft, can hang indefinitely. That means they are perfect spots for satellites to sit. There are five Lagrangian points linked to the Sun, Earth and Moon, but there are similar points anywhere that stars and planets interact.

Parking spaces in space

The first three, all lying on a line, were tentatively identified by Euler. The first, L_1, lies between the Sun and Earth, about a million miles from Earth. The Solar and Heliospheric Observatory (SOHO) sits here, viewing the Sun all the time. L_2 lies a million miles from Earth in the opposite direction, beyond the Moon's outer limit. This is where NASA's Wilkinson Microwave Anisotropy Probe (WMAP) sat as it measured the cosmic background radiation left over from the Big Bang. L_3 lies behind the sun, opposite the Earth. Scientists can see no use as yet for this point since it is hidden by the Sun.

All of these first three points are highly unstable, and it's like balancing on top of a cone for the satellites parked there; they continually make small adjustments to stay in place. But in 1772, Lagrange discovered two more points, L_4 and L_5, lying at an angle to the Earth-Sun axis and forming a triangle with it. These two points are so stable that dust and asteroids accumulate here, including the Greek and Trojan asteroids.

Some have even suggested that the L_4 and L_5 points are so stable they could be the site of an artificial colony in space. One day, if the Earth becomes too much to bear, you might go to L...

CAN AN ANT TELL IF IT'S ON A BALL?

GAUSSIAN CURVATURE

1796

ASSOCIATED
MATHEMATICIAN:
Carl Friedrich Gauss

CONCLUSION:
The angles of a triangle on
a curved surface like a ball
do not add up to 180°

Carl Friedrich Gauss was born in 1777 in Brunswick, now part of Germany. His illiterate mother never recorded the date of his birth, but remembered that it was a Wednesday, eight days before the Feast of Ascension, which is 39 days after Easter. Gauss worked out a formula for finding the date of Easter, and so calculated that he must have been born on 30 April.

Add the numbers from one to 100

Possibly the most famous story about Gauss is that when he was seven, a teacher gave his class the problem of finding the sum of all the numbers up to 100; that is $1 + 2 + 3 + 4 + ... + 100$. The young Carl Friedrich produced the answer in seconds: 5,500.

What he probably did was imagine all the numbers written out in a line, and then all the same numbers written in the reverse order underneath. He then added all the columns:

This gives a total of $100 \times 101 = 10,100$ for the sum of 1 to 100 twice; so the answer to the original question is half of 10,100, or 5,500. Gauss was smart enough to work this out in his head – or perhaps he had done the puzzle before.

Gaussian curvature

Fundamental geometry, as described by Euclid (see page 34), always refers to flat surfaces or planes, in which, for example, the interior angles of a triangle add up to 180°. On curved surfaces, however, this is no longer true.

Consider a model of the Earth. The Greenwich meridian and the 90° west meridian meet at the north pole at 90°. They both meet the equator at 90°. So the angles inside this triangle add up to 3 × 90° = 270° rather than 180°. Gauss called this sort of geometry 'Non-Euclidian geometry'.

Gauss himself described how an ant, crawling on the surface of a large sphere, could not easily tell whether the surface was flat or curved, but it could draw a triangle and see whether the angles added up to 180°.

The Duke of Brunswick heard about Gauss's brilliance, and sent him to the University of Göttingen, where at the age of 19 he made a discovery that rocked the mathematical community.

Heptadecagon

Pierre de Fermat had studied a set of numbers of the form $F = (2^x + 1)$ where $x = 2n$. The first four of these values of F, 3, 5, 17, and 257, are all prime numbers, and are called Fermat primes.

Gauss discovered that it is possible, using a straight edge and compass only, to construct a regular polygon as long as the number of sides is equal to a Fermat prime, or a Fermat prime multiplied by two, four, eight, 16, or any other power of two. In other words, he could construct an equilateral triangle, a regular pentagon, a regular heptadecagon, and even a polygon with 257 sides.

This discovery led Gauss to decide to become a full-time mathematician, and he asked for a regular 17-sided figure to be carved on his tombstone. Unfortunately, the stonemason said it was too complicated, and would look like an incompetent circle anyway.

Triangular numbers

Triangular numbers are 1, 3, 6, 10, 15, 21 and so on; each of these numbers can be represented as an equilateral triangle of dots.

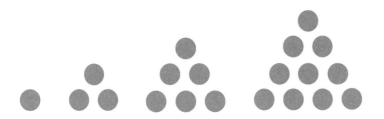

On 10 July 1796 Gauss wrote in his diary 'Eureka – num = Δ + Δ + Δ', which referred to the discovery that every number is the sum of at most three triangular numbers.

So

5 = 3 + 1 + 1,

7 = 6 + 1,

27 = 21 + 6,

and so on.

Equilateral triangle made of dots

Prime distribution

Gauss, like many other mathematicians, was fascinated by prime numbers and how they are distributed. Predicting the next prime is extraordinarily difficult, but after looking at tables of primes Gauss was struck by a curious pattern. After the first ten thousand or so, every time he multiplied N by 10 he had to add 2.3 to the average number of non-primes between the primes. This looked like a logarithmic relationship – adding instead of multiplication (see page 63).

Gauss had drawn up his findings as a table when he was 15, and realized he could calculate various features of primes using logs to base e. Thus up to the number N, about one in $\ln(N)$ would be primes, and the number of primes below N would be about $N/\ln(N)$. This relationship was a major breakthrough in number theory.

CHAPTER 5: Life-Saving, Logic and Experiments: 1797 – 1899

This was the era of big machines – The Industrial Revolution. Bigger machines meant more powerful experiments. And the findings from these experiments needed maths to explain them. Indeed, experiments with heat led Fourier to his results on sine waves. This worked two ways however, and some mathematicians, like Charles Babbage, looked at these machines and wondered how they could help mathematics, laying the groundwork for the inventions of the following century.

Yet, this era also saw an increased interest in a diverse range of more abstract maths. Perhaps the most abstract branch of mathematics from this period is topology, the study of de-forming geometric objects – treating them like modelling clay. But just because they were abstract, didn't mean they had little practical use. Boole's mathematical logic seemed as abstract as they come, using algebra to solve problems of logic. And yet, Boolean algebra is fundamentally at play in nearly all the technology we use today.

1807

ASSOCIATED MATHEMATICIAN:

Jean-Baptiste Fourier

CONCLUSION:

In trying to work out the propagation of heat, Fourier invented one of the most powerful and ubiquitous mathematical tools of today.

HOW DID WAVES LEAD TO THE GREENHOUSE EFFECT?

THE FOURIER TRANSFORM

When you hear a ringing note on a piano, the sound travels to you through the air. It moves by alternately compressing and stretching the air, pushing air molecules together and pulling them apart very rapidly. But you have no sense of your ear being buffeted to and fro. All you hear is a beautiful sound. The structure of nerve endings in your ear transforms the movement of the air into an audible tone.

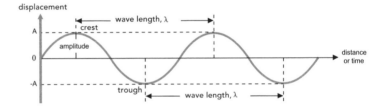

Parts of a sine wave

Fourier transforms

There are such transformations, from a signal such as sound waves to an output such as sound, in almost every conceivable part of the universe. Waves are simply repeated disturbances that spread out and transfer energy, and countless movements can be described as waves – not just sound, but electromagnetism, heat, radio, ripples on a lake, movements in the stock market and much more. Thanks to a remarkable piece of analysis by French mathematician Jean-Baptiste Fourier in 1807 called the Fourier transform, we have the mathematical tools to capture these waves just as the ear transforms sound waves into a musical tone. Fourier transforms turn complex vibrations into simple symmetrical curves on a graph called sine waves. They are brought into play whenever scientists want to study a complex fluctuation. A Fourier transform is a wonderful mathematical tool for sifting out the true signal from background noise, whether it is radiation from a distant galaxy in astronomy or the compression of digital images on the web.

Born in Auxerre, France, in 1768, Fourier grew up in the shadow of the French Revolution, and was active in promoting its aims. He was imprisoned briefly in 1795 for challenging its violent methods but recovered his position enough to be appointed as head of the famous École Polytechnique. And in 1798, he was taken to Egypt by Napoleon as scientific advisor. He loved the extreme heat there and when he returned to France in 1801 he kept his room ludicrously hot, and wrapped himself in warm clothes all the time.

After being made governor of Grenoble by Napoleon, Fourier began to experiment on how heat moves through a metal rod, and he published his initial findings in 1807 in a key paper, *Mémoire sur la propagation de la chaleur dans les corps solides* (*Treatise on the Propagation of Heat in Solid Bodies*), then followed this up in 1822 with a more substantial study, *Théorie analytique de la chaleur (Analytical Theory of Heat)*.

Modelling heat

Various mathematicians had modelled heat movement mathematically before using trigonometry (which looks at angles on graphs) and had come up with the sine wave. The graph shows time against variations in intensity, and the sine wave shows oscillations or regular displacements (such as the movement of air molecules in a sound) as a beautiful symmetrical up-and-down curve. The sine of the angle of the curve matches the intensity of the displacement. What Fourier did was show how you could transform a range of complex oscillations into simple sine waves.

When a sound hits your ear, the wave is a complex tangle of frequencies and amplitudes – pitch and intensity. What your ear does is sift them out and transform them into nerve signals that give an intelligible tone. Fourier transforms do this mathematically using a basic partial differential equation, called the heat equation, to change a complex signal into a sine wave. And every time you compress a digital photo into a .jpeg, you are using a method that relies on a Fourier transform.

Fourier was only interested in heat, but it was soon realized how widely the technique could be applied. Forty-five years later, the celebrated physicist Lord Kelvin wrote:

> *Fourier's theorem is not only one of the most beautiful results of modern analysis, but it may be said to furnish an indispensable instrument in the treatment of nearly every recondite question in modern physics.*

The greenhouse effect

Fourier's fascination with heat movement led him to another significant discovery, though – the greenhouse effect. Fourier's curiosity was aroused in the 1820s by experiments done in the previous century with so-called 'hot boxes' by Horace-Bénédict de Saussure. The hot box was a wooden box lined with black cork and exposed to sunlight. De Saussure created three separate compartments in the box, and saw that temperature rose most in the centre compartment.

Fourier realized that this was because of the way heat is both absorbed and lost. He created his own glass hot box. Over time, the air in the box became warmer than the air around it, suggesting that the glass lets sunlight in but traps heat. He surmised that the Earth behaves in the same way. Sunlight enters the atmosphere and warms the Earth up, like the sunlight shining through the glass, but like the glass, gases in the atmosphere prevent some warmth from escaping back into space. Because his model was rather like a greenhouse, this came to be called the 'greenhouse effect.'

WHY DO VIBRATIONS MAKE PATTERNS?

FIRST STEPS IN MATHEMATICAL ELASTICITY

1815

ASSOCIATED
MATHEMATICIANS:
Marie-Sophie Germain

CONCLUSION:
Germain made huge
progress in mathematical
elasticity, despite
attempts to stop her.

Among the most beautiful experiments ever conducted were those of the German physicist Ernst Chladni on vibrating plates. Chladni scattered sand on metal plates, then played the plates with a violin bow. Instantly, the sand danced and settled into a wonderful array of patterns, known as Chladni figures. The effect was so extraordinary that it seemed almost magical.

Napoleon thought so too when Chladni strummed his plates before him in 1808. The emperor instantly offered a prize of a kilogram of gold to the mathematician who could explain what was happening. Yet most mathematicians were so daunted by the problem that they shied away from it, despite the lure of the prize. One young woman, though – Marie-Sophie Germain – wholeheartedly threw herself into solving the problem, and in doing so came up with a major breakthrough in the maths of elasticity and how metals bend and spring back under stress.

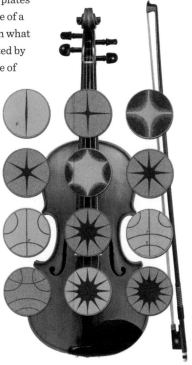

Unladlylike

Marie-Sophie (Sophie for short) Germain is one of the most extraordinary figures in the history of mathematics. Born in Paris in 1776, she was just 13 when the Revolution struck. Confined to the house, Sophie became absorbed in the mathematics books she found in her father's library. But her growing passion for maths was not ladylike, and her parents took away her warm clothes and fire to stop her studying at night. So she just shivered under the bedclothes and read even more intently until her parents relented.

She enrolled in the Ecole Polytechnique under a male pseudonym, Auguste Le Blanc, but was eventually forced to reveal her identity to the course supervisor, the brilliant mathematician Joseph-Louis Lagrange, who was so impressed with her mathematical abilities that he became a lifelong supporter.

The prize

One of the problems for Germain was that, as a woman, she was denied entry to the full range of training, and so her work was often flawed by elementary mistakes that distracted from its true genius. Nonetheless, inspired by the work of Euler, she created an equation for elasticity and in 1811, she submitted the work to the Institute of France which was judging the prize. But the basic flaws meant that although she was the only entrant, she failed to win, and the prize was rolled over to the following year.

This time, Lagrange chipped in with an equation that supported her analysis. Although she could demonstrate that Lagrange's equation did indeed generate several Chladni patterns, the mathematical background was deemed incomplete. So, for a second time, Germain, the only entrant, was denied the prize, receiving merely an honourable mention.

Then, in 1815, the prize was offered for a third time, and at last Germain was awarded it. But it was a bittersweet occasion. Yes, she had finally won, providing answers in a quest that had deterred all other mathematicians. But shortly before the ceremony, Siméon Poisson, one of the prize judges who was himself working on elasticity, wrote a curt note telling her that her analysis was flawed and lacked mathematical rigour.

Nonetheless, she continued her work on elasticity, and submitted a major paper to the institute in 1825. But the institute, whose committee included Poisson, ignored it and the paper was lost for 55 years before finally emerging in 1880 and revealing just what significant progress Germain had made in the maths of elasticity.

Rediscovery

One of her fellow mathematicians, Augustin-Louis Cauchy (1789–1857), read Germain's lost paper and advised her to publish. In 1822, Cauchy wrote a groundbreaking paper showing how stress waves move through an elastic material. This paper marks the start of the science of 'continuum mechanics', which looks at materials as a continuous whole rather than as collections of particles. It is impossible not to imagine that Germain's work was a major influence.

What Germain's work also did was show that the patterns appeared on the Chladni plates because these are the only places that are not moving. As the violin bow sets the plate vibrating, the sand is gradually jiggered to the few dead spots, and settles and accumulates there. The pattern of these dead points is dictated by the way the plate bends very slightly when rubbed by the violin bow. The plate doesn't just bend once, of course; it oscillates, bending slightly back and forth, like a twanged ruler. So the very slight distortion to the plate is a vibration that spreads as waves through the plate.

Germain's work summed up the shape of these waves of elasticity by stating 'at a point on the surface the elasticity is proportional to the sum of the principal radii of curvature of a surface at that point'. A final paper brought her ideas on curvature and elasticity together and helped lead to the discovery of the laws of equilibrium and movement of elastic solids, the laws you can see in action in soap bubbles.

For the remainder of her life, Germain devoted herself to Fermat's Last Theorem (see page 165). She came up with one of the first partial proofs, and identified a particular kind of prime number, now called Sophie Germain primes, which played a part in the final solution to the conundrum in the 1990s.

1832

ARE THERE ANY
SOLUTIONS?

CONCLUSION:

A brilliant life cut short gave us group theory, a powerful tool in solving complex equations.

A NEW WAY TO SOLVE EQUATIONS

The story of Evariste Galois's discovery of the power of symmetry in solving complex equations is at once one of the most inspiring and tragic in the history of mathematics.

Galois grew up in the aftermath of the collapse of the Napoleonic Empire in France and as a teenager was an ardent republican, which often got him into scrapes. He was a brilliant, highly imaginative boy, whose insights into mathematical problems were scrawled often indecipherably on scraps of paper.

Scraps of genius

His teachers had no idea that, on these rough scraps, Galois was making one of the great mathematical breakthroughs of the age. Galois was fascinated by complex equations. In particular, he was intrigued by the limitations of solving complex equations using algebraic formulae as mathematicians did at the time. Very quickly, he proved that while algebraic solutions can be found for quadratic, cubic and quartic equations – equations with squares, cubes and fourth powers – they cannot for quintic equations and beyond.

By the time he was 16 he had laid out an entirely revolutionary way of solving these complex equations. Galois submitted papers on his ideas to the French Academy of Sciences three times between 1829 and 1831. The first two times, the

papers went astray, and the third was returned with a rejection report from one of the judges, Siméon-Denis Poisson – the same judge who had written so critically of Sophie Germain's work (see previous entry)– saying that Galois's work was incomprehensible, and (wrongly) contained major errors.

Tragic twists

By this time, the July Revolution had driven Charles X, the last Bourbon king, into exile, and the 'Citizen King' Louis-Phillipe was on the throne. Galois's life was struck by a terrible personal tragedy when his father committed suicide. Possibly distressed by his father's death and the constant rejection of his ideas, Galois threw himself into pro-Republican activism. He was arrested twice, and when caught a third time near the Bastille with a loaded rifle, pistols and daggers, he was sent to prison, where he was badly treated by some of the inmates, and attempted suicide.

On his release in April 1832, he fell in love with a girl called Stéphanie-Felice du Motel. They exchanged letters and there are scrawled mentions of Stéphanie in Galois's mathematical notes. But things clearly did not go well. On 30 May, Galois was involved in a duel, shot and died soon after, barely 20 years old.

Things in common

Perhaps anticipating his death, Galois had sat up all the previous night writing up his ideas, and it is on these desperately written notes that his place in history rests. It is here that Galois explains that complex equations can be solved by looking at symmetries and patterns rather than trying, hopelessly, to tease things out algebraically.

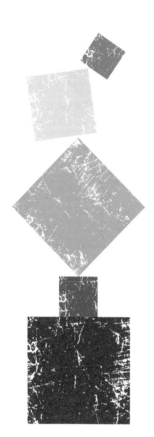

What is $\sqrt{4}$, for instance? The obvious answer is two. But it can also be -2. Though there is a difference between the solutions, there is a symmetry, as -2 is just plus 2 turned round. Galois had the brilliant insight that you did not need to break things down to find solutions but instead work with different parts or 'groups' and swap them round in different permutations.

The power of symmetries

The idea of symmetries is crucial. A square, for instance, is symmetrical in many ways. Revolve it through 90° and it still looks the same. Turn it right over, and it still looks the same. But turn it over one way and you end up with one orientation. Turn it over another and it ends up facing the other way. Rubik's Cubes are a well-known example of this kind of symmetry rotation. Galois was, of course, not talking about actual squares or cubes but groups of terms, but the idea is the same; solving equations becomes rather like solving a Rubik's Cube by playing with combinations. It was an astonishingly brilliant insight.

It took a long while for the true significance of Galois's ideas to sink in. In the twentieth century, 'group' theory became a major branch of mathematics, and a whole array of different kinds of groups have emerged since.

Galois today

In 2008, the Abel Prize, one of the key prizes in maths, went to professors John Griggs Thompson and Jacques Tits 'for their profound achievements in algebra and in particular for shaping modern group theory', which revealed something of the vast scope of groups. Their debt to Galois was plain, almost two centuries on.

Even more significantly, group theory has become the maths for understanding the subatomic world, as it helps physicists plot symmetries across different particles and interactions. Quantum physics would be impossible without Galois's maths.

CAN A MACHINE MAKE TABLES?

THE FIRST MECHANICAL COMPUTERS

1837

ASSOCIATED
MATHEMATICIANS:
Charles Babbage,
Ada Lovelace

CONCLUSION:
Babbage's ideas about
mechanical calculators
helped Lovelace create
the precursors to
computer programs.

An undergraduate at Cambridge University in 1810, Charles Babbage was sitting in the library with a table of logarithms, when he had a brilliant notion about how to solve the problem of mistakes in these tables.

A machine to end mistakes

The first tables of logarithms were produced by John Napier (see page 63). He had spent years calculating the values of these logs, and hundreds of people relied on them for their calculations. The problem with such tables is that it is all too easy for the person doing the original calculation to make a mistake – to write three instead of two, or to miss out a digit altogether. Humans make mistakes. Mistakes in tables cause untold errors later on, when people use them – not only missing buses but calculating wrong answers to complex problems.

Suppose you could get a machine to compile the tables? Then there would be no mistakes. No missed buses. No problems down the line. Babbage started by supposing he wanted to calculate the squares of all the whole numbers; they start off $1 \times 1 = 1$, $2 \times 2 = 4$, $3 \times 3 = 9$, $4 \times 4 = 16$. To begin with it's easy, but it gets harder when you want, say, 279×279. But look at the differences between the squares: 1, 3, 5, 7, 9. They are sequential odd numbers. So to find the next square, all you have to do is add the next odd number: from $5^2 = 25$, add $(5 + 6 = 11)$ to make 36. Then add $(6 + 7)$ to make 49.

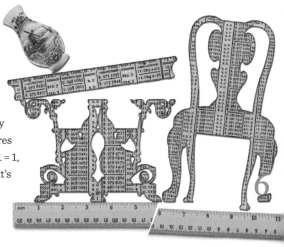

109

The difference engine

Babbage designed his machine to add or subtract these differences, and he called it a 'difference engine'. In 1822 he made a simple six-wheel model difference engine, and it worked! The Royal Society was impressed, and the Astronomical Society gave him its first-ever gold medal.

To build the real thing Babbage needed serious funding. He persuaded the Chancellor of the Exchequer to put up £1,500. Unfortunately, Babbage thought this was just an advance; the government thought it was the entire cost. But at least he was able to start making his difference engine.

Babbage never completed his machine. The precision of the engineering he demanded was almost beyond the technology of the time; he got into a terrible dispute with his engineer, Joseph Clement; and he kept going abroad to chase other dreams. In the end the government gave him £17,000, an astonishing amount, but still not enough; he kept demanding more money.

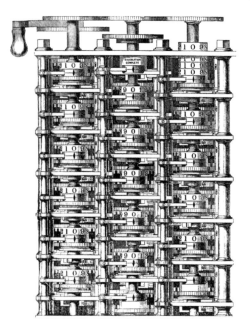

Babbage's machine

The analytical engine

To make things worse, in the late 1820s, while the argument was still going on, Babbage conceived the idea for an even better machine, the 'analytical engine', which would have been a programmable computer. Not surprisingly he could not get any financial backing, and the machine would have remained entirely in his mind, but for the assistance of Ada Lovelace.

Babbage's analytical engine would have taken instructions on punched cards, in what we now call a program. Lovelace described the 'store' or memory, and the 'mill' or central processing unit, and she speculated about what the machine might be capable of. It would not produce original ideas, but it would greatly help the advance of science, and it might be helpful in composing music, she thought.

Ada Lovelace

In 1833 Ada Lovelace, daughter of the great romantic poet George Gordon, Lord Byron, met Babbage and was fascinated by his ideas for calculating machines. In 1842 she translated a lecture he had given in Turin, and at Babbage's suggestion added her own notes. In the end her notes were three times as long as the paper, and they provide the best information we have about the potential of his analytical engine.

Most importantly, Lovelace described in detail exactly what instructions the engine would need to perform a number of complex mathematical calculations. She was the first person to write down such ideas, and she can therefore reasonably be described as the world's first computer programmer.

The first computer program

Babbage was ultimately unsuccessful in his attempt to use machines to produce more accurate tables of logarithms. He published fairly accurate tables of logarithms but these had been calculated and compiled by hand. Neither of his machines was built and it would be a hundred years before machines were used in the way he envisaged. While Babbage never got to see his ideas come to fruition, the groundwork he and Lovelace laid paved the way for the computing developments of the twentieth and twenty-first centuries. Computers are now a fundamental part of mathematical research. As well as providing more accurate results, as Babbage had intended, computers have saved recent mathematicians a huge amount of time that would have otherwise been spent performing tedious calculations.

These advances have freed up time during mathematical research for humans to concentrate on more conceptual ideas. The Great Internet Mersenne Prime Search (GIMPS), for example, is a network of computers searching for the largest prime numbers. Without the work of Babbage and Lovelace, these prime numbers would have to be found by hand. Rather than spending their time looking for primes, mathematicians are now free to study their nature and look for patterns in their distribution.

1847

ASSOCIATED
MATHEMATICIAN:

George Boole

WHAT ARE THE LAWS OF THOUGHT?

CONCLUSION:

Boolean algebra created
a logic that followed
mathematical laws.

THE INVENTION OF BOOLEAN ALGEBRA

In 1847, a little-known Lincolnshire schoolmaster intervened in a dispute between two mathematicians – and developed an extended answer that turned out to be an entirely new way of thinking about the world: a way of thinking called the algebra of logic. Without this, none of our modern computer technology could ever have been developed.

Of course the schoolmaster was no ordinary schoolmaster. His name was George Boole, and although he was still just a teacher out in the sticks, he had begun to make his mark in mathematical circles. But it was his work on the algebra of logic, now known as Boolean algebra, that was to earn him lasting fame and an appointment as the first professor of maths at Cork University.

The reason for maths

It was in Cork that Boole developed his initial ideas from Lincoln, set forth in a treatise called the *Mathematical Analysis of Logic*, into a full-blown theory expressed in a paper usually referred to as 'Laws of Thought' (1854). Boole's great insight was to find a way to use algebra to create a system that could be applied universally to any logical argument.

The idea of mathematical logic had been gradually growing in the previous half century but it was Boole who put it on its feet. Ideas about systematic logic developed thousand of years ago, most notably in the writings of Aristotle. Aristotle's system included famously the syllogism in which a combination of two assumptions or 'premises', a major and minor, leads to a conclusion. You might say, for instance: All birds lay eggs (major premise); hens are birds (minor premise); so hens lay eggs (conclusion).

New logic

Boole understood that maths works in the same way, so his idea was to reframe philosophical logic so that it could be expressed with the same simple precision of maths. His aim was to create an all-encompassing system of thought that could be applied universally, just as maths could be deployed to a wide range of numerical problems.

His method was to replace the operations in maths such as addition and subtraction with simple word equivalents that served the same functions but could be applied to any line of reasoning. In time, he realized that premises could be treated as simple algebraic symbols such as X or Y, and everything can be reduced to just three functions: AND, OR and NOT.

X and Y, for example, are sets, and when the two have things in common they are X AND Y. This is similar in arithmetic terms to X × Y. When X and Y have nothing in common it would X OR Y, similar in arithmetic terms to X + Y.

So if X represents all green objects and Y represents all round objects, this is summed up as X × Y, or XY, and XY is all objects that are both green and round. And since objects that are green and round are also those objects that are round and green, you can say XY = YX. Where every X is also a Y, the law of combination of classes gives XY = X, or even XX = X, or $X^2 = X$. That last equation doesn't apparently work in arithmetic, but there's no problem with it in Boole's logic.

Similarly if the classes are mutually exclusive such as men (X) and women (Y), you'd put X + Y. And of course you can say X + Y = Y + X.

And if you wanted to add a new category, such as French (Z), you could say: Z(X +Y) = ZY + ZX. In other words, all French men and women is the same as all French men and all French women. If Z (French) contains all French women (Y) you could write all French people but the women as Z NOT Y, or Z - Y.

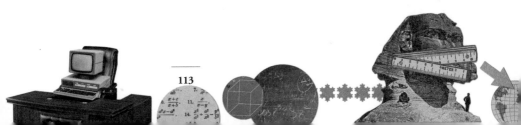

Boole games

What was astonishing was that these simple connections to maths are there in the language and seem almost banally obvious. And yet no one had actually drawn attention to them before Boole. It was a truly remarkable insight, and one of genuine genius. Although Boole's genius was recognized in his time, it took decades before the staggering scope of his insight was realized. He lived quietly in Ireland making other great contributions to maths, but none quite as significant as this. What he had done was create a system not only translating for all ideas into very simple arithmetic, but a way for evaluating them, too.

After Boole's death, his ideas fell largely into the shadows for 70 years or so. Then, in the 1930s, young Claude Shannon, working for Bell Telephones, was looking for a way to reduce signals to the essential information to avoid the problem of noise on long distance calls. When he rediscovered Boole, he realized Boole's work gave a key insight into information. Inspired by Boole's simple logic he realized that it was indeed possible to strip all information down to just 1s and 0s – binary digits – a flash of genius that was to launch the computer age.

CAN STATISTICS SAVE LIVES?

STATISTICAL ANALYSIS AND MEDICAL REFORM

1856

ASSOCIATED
MATHEMATICIAN:
Florence Nightingale

CONCLUSION:
Statistics were used to improve conditions in hospitals, saving many lives as a result.

At a time when women were excluded from England's universities, Florence Nightingale received a full academic education in her enlightened home. She had a passion for order and data: aged nine, she kept detailed records of produce from the family vegetable garden. As a young woman, she met leading intellectual figures of the time, such as Charles Babbage (see page 109), and was exposed to the new discipline of statistics.

During the Victorian age, new technologies of printing and communication meant that 'Big Data' could be collected and studied. The ease of gathering new data necessitated mathematical advancements to understand the data fully and identify patterns within it.

Novel ways of representing data – bar charts and pie charts – came to Nightingale's attention, as did pioneering ideas of using data to investigate social issues. She began to wonder how quantitative evidence could drive changes in policy, especially in public health. Nightingale felt a humanitarian calling to work as a nurse – unusual for a woman of her background – and saw it as a perfect setting to test her ideas. She became an unpaid superintendent of a women's hospital on Harley Street in 1853. The following March saw the outbreak of the Crimean War.

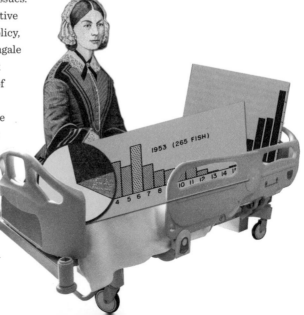

Sanitary reform

During conflict, the vast majority of deaths were due to disease – perhaps 10 times more likely to kill than a wound. Many of these diseases were preventable. It now seems obvious that with better diet, hygiene and sanitation, lives would be saved, although this did not seem evident to the medical and military establishment of the day.

In November 1854 Nightingale arrived at the army hospital in Scutari, Constantinople. Conditions there were appalling: in that first winter over 4,000 patients perished, and as she later wrote, 'Our soldiers were enlisted to die in the barracks.' Beyond the obvious squalor, Nightingale saw its underlying cause: administrative chaos. On top of the filth and malnutrition, there was no coordination of treatment and little chance for the patients.

Nightingale immediately began to collect data systematically: standardized medical notes, consistent classifications of illnesses, accurate recording of diet, time to recovery for the luckier patients. Based on solid data, the solution became obvious: thorough 'sanitary reform' of the hospital and rigorous training of nursing staff. Mortality rates of 60 per cent dropped to two per cent during her tenure and she returned to Britain a hero, celebrated in verse as 'The Lady with the Lamp'. But she was also the lady with the data.

Convincing coxcombs

Then as now, data can be hard to grasp. Collecting hard evidence is one thing, but another of Nightingale's great achievements was to invent a graphical representation that made the data vivid enough to persuade politicians to take action – the reforms she wanted to see were not going to be cheap. She took an earlier idea, the pie chart, and developed the polar area diagram, which she called a 'coxcomb' (see opposite).

It conveys a large amount of information. Areas of the sectors depict death rates in a given month, the overall size of the diagram giving the annual picture. You can see immediately the effect of the sanitary reforms. Coloured regions show cause of death. The blue sector (measured to the centre of the

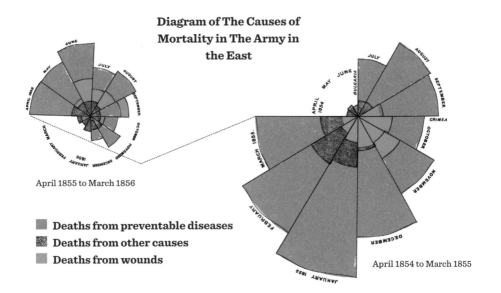

Diagram of The Causes of Mortality in The Army in the East

April 1855 to March 1856

- Deaths from preventable diseases
- Deaths from other causes
- Deaths from wounds

April 1854 to March 1855

diagram) indicates mortality due to preventable diseases. It is overlapped by a smaller black sector ('other causes') and, on top, a red sector ('deaths from wounds'). It is obvious that wounds were the least likely thing to kill you. A visual, colour-coded reference proved far more arresting and informative than comparing figures in a table and led to widespread medical reform.

A medical statistician nowadays might criticize this data. Firstly, it comes from an open clinical trial of the sanitary reforms. How do we know that the death rate didn't fall for other reasons: better weather, or fewer mosquitoes, say? Secondly, how bad were these figures by the standards of the day? Nightingale addressed this by adding a circle giving comparable average mortality in England: Victorian hospitals were definitely dangerous, and military hospitals worst of all. Finally, we might ask: could survival rates have improved purely by chance? Were they statistically significant or not? This also seems obvious, but at the time it was impossible to prove. As the first woman elected to the Royal Statistical Society, Nightingale advocated further progress in statistics that eventually made it possible to be sure.

Nightingale's coxcombs

117

1858

ASSOCIATED MATHEMATICIANS:
August Möbius and Johann Benedict Listing

CONCLUSION:
The simple-looking Möbius strip revolutionized the mathematics of shape.

HOW MANY SIDES AND HOW MANY EDGES?

THE BIRTH OF TOPOLOGY

The Möbius strip is one of the most curious shapes ever invented. You can make one just by cutting out a strip of paper, looping it round, then twisting one end round before sticking it to the other end. It couldn't be simpler, yet it is at the heart of a conundrum that helped launch an entire branch of mathematics, topology, which studies properties of shapes and surfaces as they are bent, twisted and crumpled.

The Möbius strip

What makes the Möbius strip so mathematically fascinating is that it has just one edge and one side. It looks rather like a wristband. Indeed, you could put your hand through it and wear it like one. But a wristband has two edges and two sides. The twist in the Möbius strip changes all that. You could trace your finger along the edge and after going twice round you are back where you started – so it must have only one edge. The famous artist of impossible shapes, Maurits Cornelis Escher, once did a sketch of one with ants crawling round it on a seemingly endless journey.

It seems to be the embodiment of infinity, and mathematicians went on to create other 'infinite' shapes, like the Klein bottle. For some, the Möbius strip has a symbolic mystery. 'Our lives are Möbius strips,' wrote Joyce Carol Oates, '...misery and wonder simultaneously. Our destinies are infinite, and infinitely recurring.'

Actually, you can create some interesting effects by cutting a paper Möbius strip with scissors. If you cut along the centre line, mind-bendingly, you don't get two loops but a single bigger loop with two twists. Yet if you cut along a line a third of the way from one edge, you do get two loops – one fat loop the same size as the original and one loop thin and twice as big. Oh, and they are interlinked, too.

But the strip is much more than a party trick. It was invented independently in the 1850s by German mathematicians Johann Benedict Listing and August Möbius. The invention marked the starting point of topology, and it was no coincidence that Listing and Möbius came up with the idea around the same time. Both men were students of the great German mathematician Carl Friedrich Gauss, and it may even be that Gauss invented the strip and gave the idea to both of his students.

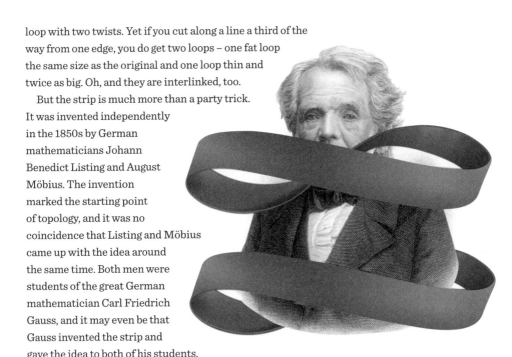

The birth of topology

Until then, shapes without regular, geometric sides that could be measured were viewed as rather taboo. Back in 1735, Leonhard Euler's solution for the problem of the Königsberg bridges depended not on measurements but the layout of the key points, so this was the very first topological discovery. But it remained something of a curiosity, rather than the start of something big. The brilliant Gauss did a lot of groundwork on topology but kept it entirely under wraps for fear of ridicule.

The Möbius strip, then, was not an out-of-the-blue discovery but part of a larger investigation of his two students into topological shapes. Indeed, Listing coined the word *topology*, from the Greek *topos*, meaning place. And the strip came up as an answer to the question, 'Is it possible to create a three-dimensional shape with a single side and a single edge?'

At the time, significantly, August Möbius was studying polyhedra: solids with many faces. Euler had first highlighted

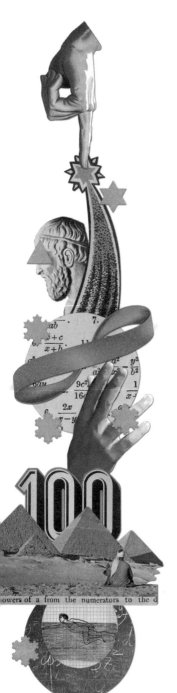

these shapes in 1750 in a letter to Goldbach in which he provides a general equation for them: $v - e + f = 2$
In this equation, v is the number of vertices of the polyhedron, e is the number of edges and f is the number of faces. In 1813, little-known Swiss mathematician Simon Antoine Jean L'Huilier had realized that Euler's formula was wrong for solids with holes in them, and came up with a new equation showing that in a solid with g holes, $v - e + f = 2 - 2g$.

It was this that Möbius was looking at, and we'll return to the issue of holes shortly.

Holes in a solid

In the time since its discovery, topologists have learned how the strip fits into a broader understanding of shapes. One key factor is the number of holes, for instance, which allows topologists to identify different genuses. A shape with no hole like a lollipop is genus 0. A coffee cup and a doughnut are both genus 1. Because both objects have just one hole, the cup can be deformed into a doughnut just by stretching and bending – theoretically, that is, but you might imagine it done with plasticine.

Yet a Möbius strip and a wristband also both have one hole, so genus alone is not enough to distinguish them. What distinguishes them is that the strip is 'non-orientable' whereas the wristband is 'orientable'. When you (or an ant) cross an orientable surface, it will always end up the same way round. But on a non-orientable surface, the ants, as on Escher's Möbius strip, end up flipped the other way round like a mirror image.

The discovery of the Möbius strip and the subsequent mushrooming of topology has opened up new ways to study the natural world. A branch of topology called knot theory, for instance, has played a key role in understanding how the coils of DNA in living things unravel. It comes into string theory, too, as it explores the fundamental nature of matter. And it provokes new mathematical discoveries. In 2018, the Fields Medal went to Akshay Venkatesh for his work on integrating topology with other fields such as number theory.

WHICH CIRCLE DOES IT GO IN?

VENN DIAGRAMS

1881

ASSOCIATED
MATHEMATICIAN:
John Venn

CONCLUSION:
Venn diagrams are more
than just simple graphs.

Few mathematical ideas have seeped into the public consciousness like Venn diagrams, created by John Venn in 1881. They've become a brilliantly useful way of graphically grouping things and showing the overlap between them, whether it's ideas on what makes someone datable, or categories of atomic particles. John Venn, the humble British mathematician and professor of logic who created them, would have been utterly astonished if he had known what would happen to his diagrams after he dryly presented them to the world in an obscure paper entitled 'On the Diagrammatic and Mechanical Representation of Propositions and Reasonings'.

Nowadays, the use of Venn diagrams has extended far beyond mathematics, but Venn's idea was a simple mathematical tool, though it was in tune with cutting-edge mathematical thinking. Symbolic logic was very much in the air at the time with Boole's introduction of his Boolean algebra (see page 112) with its AND, OR, NOT connections. So, too, was set theory, after Georg Cantor and Richard Dedekind's groundbreaking work in the mid-1870s.

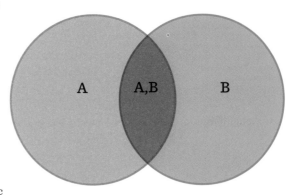

A logic system

Venn was looking to present a system of mathematical logic with his diagrams. Venn diagrams look at sets of things with something in common, such as genuses of animals. Each set is

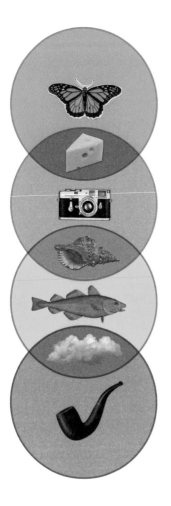

given its own circle and the circles are overlapped. (These can be very roughly drawn, even oval). Objects in each set, known as 'elements', are arranged in the circles so that objects that belong to both sets are placed in the area where the circles overlap. One circle might be for swimming animals such as fish. Another for walking animals might contain kinds of mammals. Animals that swim and walk such as otters are placed in the overlap.

But this not simply a nice graphic presentation. The circles represent stages of formal logic. Two-circle Venn diagrams are categorical propositions, such as 'All A are B', 'No A are B', 'Some A are B' and 'Some A are not B.' Three-circle diagrams, on the other hand, represent syllogisms, in which there are two categorical premises and a categorical conclusion. For example, all snakes are reptiles; all reptiles are cold-blooded animals; therefore all snakes are cold-blooded animals.

So Venn intended his diagrams not just as neat tools for classification but as a system of logical proofs. The crucial thing is deciding the set headings, usually symbolized by a capital such as X, Y or Z, and the elements of each set, usually indicated by a lower case letter x_1, x_2, x_3 and so on. If these are chosen well, the overlap gives your proof.

Ancient circles

Venn's idea was not especially original. The Catalan monk Ramon Llull had described various graphic shapes for representing logical relationships back in the 1200s, and Gottfried Liebniz mentioned using circles for classifying objects in the 1600s.

Then in 1760, Swiss mathematician Leonhard Euler wrote about how circles could represent the logical relationships between objects. Venn acknowledged his debt to Euler in his paper, and refers to 'Eulerian circles'. He also acknowledged that such circles had been known about for some time. But what Venn did was actually rather different. Euler circles show just relevant relationships between sets; Venn diagrams show all relationships.

So, for instance, you might have a diagram representing beer, low-alcohol drinks and gluten-free drinks. On a Venn diagram, there'd be three overlapping circles, showing different combinations of these three. In the middle all three combine in low-alcohol, gluten-free beer. Even if there is not actually such a drink, the Venn diagram provides for the possibility of its existence. The Euler diagram only allows circles within circles: so a low-alcohol circle within the beer circle, for instance, if all low-alcohol drinks are beers. But it could not show all the possible relationships.

Venn today

Venn diagrams have proved to be genuinely powerful tools for mathematics and logic. They are an integral part of set theory, and useful in probability studies. Mathematics is about logical relationships, and, though they seem simple, Venn diagrams can reveal relationships between sets of numbers at a fundamental level. In the last half-century, for example, Venn diagrams have proved illuminating about prime numbers. They have been used with Gray Codes (used in binary encoding developed by Bell engineer Frank Gray in 1947), with binomial coefficients, rotational symmetries, revolving-door algorithms and much more.

Flat Venns have just two or three sets, but mathematicians have created them in three or more dimensions and add extra sets. With a tesseract (a four-dimensional representation of a cube), they can make Venns with 16 symmetrically intersecting sets. And if they are willing to dispense with symmetry, they can go much higher. Even Venn himself constructed ingenious versions of up to six sets by using tubes, ellipses and circles.

But Venn diagrams have proved useful far beyond maths. They are widely used as teaching tools in schools, where teachers use them to compare and contrast different sets of ideas. Indeed, Venns are used everywhere from advertising to military planning. They've turned out to be one of the simplest but most powerful ways of structuring thought ever invented.

1899

ASSOCIATED
MATHEMATICIAN:
Henri Poincaré

CONCLUSION:
Poincaré's mistake
revolutionizes our
understanding of
chaotic systems.

WHY ARE SOME SYSTEMS CHAOTIC?

THE MATHEMATICS BEHIND CHANCE

It should have been one of the great moments in brilliant French mathematician Henri Poincaré's career. He had just won a prize awarded by King Oscar II of Sweden for his amazingly original work on the three-body problem. He had even been awarded the Légion d'Honneur for it and been elected to the French Academy of Sciences.

And then, just as his prize-winning paper was about to be published, in June 1899, a young editor, Lars Phragmén, notified them that it contained a major error. And to Poincaré's horror, Phragmén was right. The copies of the paper would have to be recalled and reprinted. That would cost him far more than the 2,500 Swedish crowns prize. Worse still, it was a hugely humiliating moment, caught in an error in the glare of the public eye. And yet, Poincaré was to turn this disaster into a revolutionary insight. At once, he admitted his error and set to work to discover where he had gone wrong. It took him many years, but his diligent efforts led him to a discovery that eventually launched a major new branch of mathematics, chaos theory – though at the time it appeared to be a dead end.

The three-body problem

Poincaré had started working on the three-body problem in 1885, determined to win the prize announced by the Swedish king. It was an old issue. How can you prove or disprove that the orbits of three-bodies interacting in space will have stable orbits? It had been done long ago with two bodies. But with three bodies there were so many variables, and the problem had defeated many great mathematical brains (see page 92).

So Poincaré decided to try a new approach. Instead of trying to follow the movement of each mass point using trigonometric series, he decided to analyse the entire system's state of motion using the new techniques of topology that he had helped develop. His method involved differential geometry, which studies graphic curves, surfaces, and manifolds (the higher-dimensional representations of surfaces). Differential geometry looks for answers to such questions as 'What is the shortest path between two points on a surface?' Poincaré used it to calculate orbits from different viewpoints in 'phase space' – that is, a space that is multidimensional because it represents all possible states of a system simultaneously. This was brilliant, cutting-edge mathematics.

Poincaré was in this way able to make great headway. But it was still an awesome problem, and to get tangible results that showed the merits of his new method, he concentrated on the restricted version of the three-body problem, in which the third body has such infinitely tiny mass that it has no gravitational effect on the other two. At last, by limiting his enquiry's scope this way, he was finally able to show stable orbits in a three-body system. The proof involved two facing 'asymptotic surfaces' – surfaces that mark the boundary between positive and negative curvature. The stability was confirmed by their meeting.

Prize and fall

The award jury accepted that it was by no means a complete solution, but they were impressed enough by the ingenuity and success of the method to have little hesitation in awarding Poincaré the prize. Then came the hammer blow. He had assumed that two asymptotic surfaces met to make a single sheet. But when he looked at it again, the surfaces could cross and recross. It was a small error, but multiplied many times, it meant his solution failed.

Poincaré painstakingly retraced his calculations, and 18 months on, he was able to publish a revised version. But as he worked, he discovered where he had gone wrong. He realized that even a very tiny change in his initial conditions would lead to vastly different orbits. Poincaré was quick to realize that it meant chance could play a huge part in a deterministic system like the Newtonian view of the universe in which everything behaves according to the laws of motion.

The motion laws of the universe cover every movement, and this implies that, given the right calculations, you should be able to entirely predict future movements. But, Poincaré wrote, 'A very small cause, which escapes our notice determines a considerable effect that we cannot fail to see, and then we say that the effect is due to chance.' In other words, some differences in movements, which are so small that they can only be called chance, may have massive effects on the outcome. So, he wrote,

'It may happen that small differences in the initial conditions produce very great ones in the final phenomena. A small error in the former will produce an enormous error in the latter. Prediction becomes impossible...'

A theory of chance

This is where he had gone wrong in his three-body calculation. But this was much more than an effort to justify his mistake. He was convinced it was a major discovery. He wrote a paper in 1899 about it and then a popular book called *Chance* in 1907. In *Chance*, he uses the word *chaos* to describe how unpredictable these small elements of chance can make some systems appear. He explains how a difference of a fraction of a millimetre in the meeting of male and female cells could change history, leading to the birth of a Napoleon, or an imbecile. Poncaré points out that chance is not incompatible with a deterministic system at all. He looks at the weather as simply the result of chance operating in the instability of the atmosphere. 'People pray for rain,' he says, 'but at the same time it is considered ridiculous to pray for an eclipse.' Really, he argues, the weather is equally as rigidly determined as the eclipse. It is just that the operation of chance with the weather is so major that we just do not have enough knowledge to predict it. Such systems seem to be chaotic, but the normal laws of the universe are still operating entirely regularly.

It was indeed a significant discovery, but most people at the time, maybe even Poincaré himself, thought of it just as an interesting curiosity. But all this changed half a century later with the discovery of the Butterfly Effect and the development of chaos theory (see page 159).

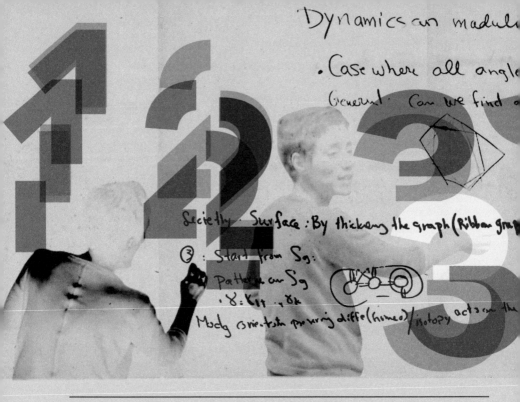

CHAPTER 6: In the Mind and the Universe: 1900 – 1949

The start of the twentieth century saw the split between applied and pure maths become more marked. It became increasingly difficult to equate mathematics with largely practical uses, like Shannon's invention of binary digital signals, with work on seemingly universal truths, like Ramanujan's ideas about pi and prime numbers. They were both undoubtedly 'mathematics', but different sides of it.

While these branches became more distinct, several American mathematicians made some of the most impactful and impressive leaps in practical mathematics as large parts of the world plunged into conflict. Von Neumann's Game Theory, refined by John Nash, remained a cornerstone of economic theory for decades after it was first conceived. Meanwhile, Shannon and Wiener took inspiration from real-life problems to lay the mathematical groundwork for some of the technology that came to define this century.

1913

ASSOCIATED MATHEMATICIAN:
Emile Borel

CONCLUSION:
Given enough time,
even the most unlikely
outcome will occur.

COULD A LOT OF MONKEYS WRITE SHAKESPEARE?

THE INFINITE MONKEY THEOREM

'Probability,' said the Irish mathematician George Boole in 1854, 'is expectation founded upon partial knowledge. A perfect acquaintance with all the circumstances affecting the occurrence of an event would change expectation into certainty.'

So, if we don't know for sure that probable events will occur, can we be sure that improbable events won't? And when does improbable become impossible? This is the question that intrigued French mathematician Emile Borel about a century ago. The impossible and improbable are embedded in our language. 'Lightning never strikes twice in the same place.' 'Oh that could never happen!' But maybe it could...

A brief history of chance

Back in the times of ancient Greece and Rome, many thinkers pondered whether the world could have been formed from atoms coming together entirely by chance. The Greek philosopher Aristotle thought it could – unlikely but possible. Roman scholar Cicero thought it so unlikely that you could be certain it didn't. We now know they were both right. Yes, countless atoms did come together but it was not entirely by chance – they were pulled by gravity.

But mathematicians like certainty, even when it comes to uncertainty, so over the centuries many have tried to pin down the impossible. There was, for instance, the eighteenth-century French philosopher Jean d'Alembert, who was told by his mother that he would never be a philosopher. D'Alembert explored whether you could measure long sequences in which occurrence and non-occurrence are equally likely. Was it possible that a tossed coin could land heads two million times in a row, for instance?

A hundred years later another Frenchman, Antoine-Augustin Cournot (1801–1877) asked if you could ever balance a cone on its tip. Of course, we've seen circus acrobats and conceptual artists perform seemingly impossible balancing acts. Cournot wanted to distinguish between a physical certainty – an event that can certainly happen physically, like the balancing cone – and a practical certainty, one that is so unlikely that is impossible in practice. He put it like this in what we now call Cournot's principle: 'It is a practical certainty that an event with a very small probability will not happen.'

The Law of Single Chance

Emile Borel wrote a series of papers about this in the 1920s. Borel was a politician and in 1925 became Minister of the Marine in the government of fellow mathematician Paul Painlevé. Who knows how much his political career influenced his interest in the impossible?

As he explored the notion of the impossible, he came up with what he called the Law of Single Chance, now known as Borel's idea, which is essentially the same as Cournot's principle. Borel argued that some events, while not mathematically impossible, are so unlikely that to all intents and purposes are impossible. Of course, there is a chance that the sun might rise in the west one day, but it is so unlikely as to be impossible.

To help pin this down, Borel created a scale on which the probability of things occurring is so small they can be considered impossible in practice. That does not mean they are mathematically impossible, but so unlikely that a mathematician can treat them as impossible. On a human scale, a probability of less than one in a million could be said to be impossible.

Monkey bards

To show how his ideas worked, Borel presented a picture of monkeys hitting typewriter keys randomly. Could they by sheer chance eventually type the entire works of Shakespeare? Of course, it is highly improbable that they will, but mathematically, over an infinite time (or with an infinite number of monkeys), it must certainly happen. So it is not mathematically impossible but so unlikely that to all intents and purposes it is impossible. As a result, Borel's law is popularly known as the Infinite Monkey Theorem.

Monkeys typing the works of Shakespeare is so captivating that it has popped up in popular culture ever since, sometimes humorously, sometimes with serious intent. Then in 2003, scientists got a grant to actually try it with monkeys. Six Celebes crested macaques in Devon's Paignton Zoo were let loose on a computer keyboard. The monkeys rightly took a dim view of the writer's life and mostly bashed the keyboard with a stone or peed on it. All the same, they ended up typing five pages, mostly of the letter 's': obviously a sign of disapproval.

In 2011, computer programmer Jesse Andersen decided to play it safe – he created a million virtual monkeys on a computer program. This army of computer monkeys then ran through 180 billion character groups a day at random. Amazingly, in just 45 days, they did indeed come up with the goods. It was, however, a bit of a cheat, because the program was made to spot and capture groups of nine correct characters in the right sequence to build up the complete works.

Mathematicians can say that such an event as the Monkey Shakespeare is impossible in practice. But impossible in practice doesn't mean never...

IS ENERGY ALWAYS CONSERVED?

DEFINING THE UNIVERSE IN TERMS OF ALGEBRA

1918

ASSOCIATED
MATHEMATICIAN:
Emmy Noether

CONCLUSION:
Cutting-edge algebra was
used to plug a big gap in
Einstein's work.

Just over a hundred years ago, a mathematician came up with a theorem that has come to shape modern physics. It was a theorem so groundbreaking that it is still predicting new insights into matter and energy. The creator of this theorem was the German mathematician Emmy Noether (1882–1935). Einstein described Noether as a 'creative mathematical genius.' And yet she is virtually unknown outside specialist circles.

This lack of fame is surely in part because of her gender. Prejudice against women among mathematicians was deep-rooted at the time, and Noether faced continual obstacles to her progress. At the University of Göttingen, where she achieved some of her greatest mathematical insights, the university authorities would not allow a woman to lecture in maths and so for four years she taught as 'David Hilbert's assistant'. Additionally her mathematics is so much at the cutting edge that it is not easy for the non-specialist to grasp just what it means.

The problem with relatives

In 1915, Einstein unleashed his Theory of General Relativity on the world. It was fiendishly hard to understand, and yet Noether's theorem, developed just a few years later, not only plugged a major hole in Einstein's theory, but also provided a profound new insight in physics conservation laws.

Newton's laws of motion revealed that the conservation of momentum was fundamental – as demonstrated in the passing on of movement of the swinging balls in a Newton's cradle. So was the law of conservation of angular momentum – the law that makes a spinning skater speed up as he pulls his arms in.

Meanwhile, the conservation of energy was also recognized in the nineteenth century as one of the deepest laws of nature. This is the idea that the total amount of energy in any system always stays the same. It can switch from one form to another but the total energy never varies. This was an insight considered so fundamental that no physical theory could ignore it.

And yet, that's effectively what Einstein's theory did. His theory included an equation for the conservation of energy, but when the brilliant German mathematicians David Hilbert and Felix Klein examined it in detail, it seemed no more meaningful than saying $x - x = 0$. They were not saying that Einstein's theory was at fault – simply that the maths wasn't creating the full picture.

They realized they needed the help of someone expert in the maths of invariants, things that don't change – like the conservation of energy. And so they called upon their colleague at Göttingen, Emmy Noether.

Whichever way you look at it

Noether was not remotely interested in the physics, and looked at the issue of conservation of energy as a purely mathematical issue. She approached it using the cutting-edge maths of transformations – what happens when an object is, for instance, enlarged, rotated and translated (moved without changing) – and also symmetries. The idea of using symmetries (similar groups of terms) to solve complex algebraic equations had been introduced by Galois a century before (see page 106). Noether's brainwave was to use symmetries to explore conservation laws just as they were used to solve algebraic equations.

Noether was quickly able to come up with two theorems; the second showed that General Relativity was indeed a special case, as Hilbert and Klein had suspected. Energy may not be conserved locally under General Relativity, but across the universe it is. It was the first theorem, however, that was truly groundbreaking.

Noether's first theorem showed that all conservation laws were part of the same bigger picture – energy, momentum, angular momentum and everything else. They are all linked by symmetry. It shows that every conservation law has an associated symmetry and vice versa. Noether's theorem provides equations for finding the symmetry that underlies each conservation law. Energy conservation is translation symmetry in time. Momentum conservation is translation symmetry in space. In other words, these conservations occur because things are the same no matter which way you turn and whether you go backward in time. Basic physical equations don't change in space or time.

Symmetry power

Noether's paper, 'Invariant Variational Problems', was unveiled on 23 July 1918. Think of it this way: if you hit a billiard ball across a table it runs straight simply because the table is flat (invariant). If the table were curved it would run differently.

Ever since Noether's breakthrough paper, the impact of her first theorem has been growing. In the 1970s, physicists put all the known particles into a framework known as the Standard Model, a framework that was built using Noether's theorem and depends on symmetry. Symmetry predicted the existence of the Higgs boson, which was finally confirmed in 2012.

Remarkably, although physicists now revere Noether for her theorem on conservation laws and symmetry, mathematicians know Noether even more for the development of abstract algebra, which focuses on the entirely theoretical study of algebraic structures. She was undoubtedly one of the greatest mathematical minds of the twentieth century.

ARE TAXICAB NUMBERS DULL?

CONCLUSION:
A self-taught
mathematician turns out
to be a genius and makes
leaps in number theory.

1,729 AND NUMBER THEORY

One day in 1916, eminent Cambridge maths professor Godfrey Harold ('GH') Hardy arrived at the sanatorium where his young protégé, the self-taught Indian maths wizard Srinivasa Ramanujan, was a patient. 'I had ridden in taxicab number 1,729,' Hardy recalled, 'and remarked that the number seemed to me rather a dull one.' Immediately, Ramanujan came back: 'No, it is a very interesting number; it is the smallest number expressible as the sum of two cubes in different ways.'
And Ramanujan was exactly right:

$$1,729 = 13 + 123 = 93 + 103$$

Ramanujan wasn't the first to notice this. Bernard de Bessy, a French mathematician, had spotted it as long ago as 1657, and some suspect Hardy was trying to cheer his friend up, knowing he wouldn't be able to resist the temptation of showing just how interesting 1,729 is.

Hailing a cab

Whatever the truth, it sparked renewed interest in the smallest numbers that are the sum of two cubes in several (n) ways, and they came to be called 'taxicab numbers'. Ever since, mathematicians have been hunting for other taxicab numbers. Hardy himself, with his colleague Edward Wright, went on to prove that it should be possible to find such numbers

for all positive integers, and their proof became the basis
for computer programs that could be set to search for such
numbers. There are in theory infinitely many taxicab numbers
but they are elusive because while a computer can find many
such numbers, it cannot locate the lowest such number: the
true taxicab number. So in over a century of searching, only
the first six lowest numbers have been found:

Ta(1): 2

Ta(2): 1729 (1657, de Bessy)

Ta(3): 87,539,319 (1957, Leech)

Ta(4): 6,963,472,309,248 (1989, Rosenstiel, Dardis and
Rosenstiel)

Ta(5): 48,988,659,276,962,496 (1994, Dardis)

Ta(6): 24,153,319,581,254,312,065,344 (2008, Hollerbach)

So the search is on for the taxicab number that can be made
from the sum of two cubes in 7 ways...

Backing your cab

Some mathematicians have gone further and started looking
at other numbers that are the sums of cubes. Taxicab numbers
are several different sums of two positive cubes. In 'cabtaxi'
numbers, the sums can include negatives. So, for instance:

$91 = 6^3 - 5^3 = 3^3 + 4^3$

Such numbers may seem arcane, and hugely difficult to dig
out. But that doesn't make them useless practically. In fact, the
very difficulty of working them out makes them fascinating to
computer programmers looking for methods of encryption.
Code numbers for bank accounts may be the sum of two cubes,
for instance – and it's almost impossible for hackers to work
out how the number is broken down into cubes. So we may have
Ramanujan and Hardy to thank for our bank security.

Letter from India

In fact, taxicab numbers were only one aspect of Ramanujan
and Hardy's work together. The partnership had started one
day in January 1913, when GH had received an extraordinary
letter. It came from Ramanujan, then a poor clerk in the offices
of the Madras port authority. Ramanujan humbly asked the

professor if he could give him some feedback on some maths calculations he had been working on.

Hardy was naturally sceptical but as he sifted through the notes he began to see a host of startling and intricate formulae about infinite series, integrals and primes. In one place, Ramanujan claimed to have discovered a function of X which was equal to the sum of all prime numbers less than X. If Ramanujan was right, it would be one of the mathematical breakthroughs of the century. But, because Ramanujan was entirely self-taught, the workings were so opaque that Hardy could not be sure whether this was the work of a genius or a fraud. After thinking it over, and talking with a colleague, he decided the answer was genius, and he at once wrote to Ramanujan inviting him to come and study in Cambridge.

Even though the proof about the function of X turned out to be flawed, Ramanujan was indeed a genius, and over the next five years, the two mathematicians worked closely together producing great work on primes. All of Ramanujan's publications under Hardy at Cambridge were conventionally written with the normal vigorous proofs expected. But his personal notebooks are rather different. Self-taught, he had no concept of strict proofs. To him what mattered were the answers.

Master switch

Ramanujan, for instance, created what he called his Master Formula. The proof of this is a chaotic mix of different methods, and yet all the results he gets using this Master Formula turn out to be correct. Ramanujan did some brilliant work on partitions (the ways numbers can be written as the sum of smaller whole numbers), and came up with a conjecture about x^{n-1}, which was linked to a major breakthrough in algebraic geometry half a century later.

It is for the taxicab numbers that he will forever be remembered, and yet it was the least original thing to spring from a mind filled to brim with mathematical creativity.

WHAT'S THE BEST WAY TO WIN?

GAME THEORY AND MATHEMATICAL STRATEGY

1928

ASSOCIATED
MATHEMATICIAN:
John von Neumann

CONCLUSION:
Game theory is a
mathematical guide to
putting self-interest first.

Game theory is a way of studying interactions mathematically as a game of strategy between two or more players each trying to win. It was the brainchild of John von Neumann, a brilliant Hungarian émigré mathematician to the USA, later pinpointed by many as the model for the unhinged nuclear scientist in Kubrick's film *Dr Strangelove*.

Von Neumann first explored the idea in 1928 in a paper called aptly '*The Theory of Parlour Games*' while still in Europe. He was inspired by card games, and the chess-like strategy games of his childhood. Poker, he reasoned, is not just a game of chance; it is a game of strategy, and the strategy is bluffing. Could, he wondered, the best bluffing strategy be pinned down mathematically?

The same theory for poker and war

Von Neumann was not the first to explore this idea. Frenchman Emile Borel wrote several papers about it in the early 1920s, discussing if mathematics could find a winning poker strategy when you have limited information about your opponents' cards. Borel imagined that such a strategy might also apply to

economic and military scenarios. And long before Borel, other thinkers had tried to apply mathematics to devise winning strategies.

But it was von Neumann who first established mathematical gaming as a complete theory. His ideas were partly inspired by strategies for deploying US forces in the Pacific in World War II, and in 1943, von Neumann began working on the Manhattan Project to develop the atom bomb. He created probability models to reduce the chances of the planes carrying the bombs being shot down, and he brought mathematics to the issue of selecting targets for maximum impact. While working on the bomb, von Neumann collaborated with fellow émigré Oskar Morgenstern to write the book that set the foundations of game theory, *Theory of Games and Economic Behaviour*. It was written in 1944, but not published until 1946, and when it came out, remarkably for a high-level maths book, it hit the newspaper front pages.

Despite origins in wartime strategy, the book focused on how economic behaviour could be treated as a game. To look at economics as he had looked at poker, von Neumann drew on 'rational choice theory', which looks at humans as 'individual rational utility maximizers' – that is, as a collection of individuals, each using logic to achieve the maximum 'utility' or personal benefit. The theory aims to predict human behaviour mathematically on the basis that we're all out for number one.

With game theory, the idea was to look at people involved in interactions as 'players' or 'agents', each intent on winning or looking for strategies to maximize rewards. 'Real life,' asserted von Neumann, 'consists of bluffing, of little tactics of deception, of asking yourself

what is the other man going to think I mean to do.' The best
way to play, he calculated was not to play to win, but to play
to minimize your losses – a strategy that became known as
'minimax' - the minimum possible maximum loss.

Should you confess to the crime?

The most famous example of the way this worked out was 'The
Prisoner's Dilemma'. Imagine you and your partner in crime
have been arrested by the police and put in separate cells. If
you protect each other by staying quiet (called 'cooperation' in
game theory), then the police's scant evidence is only enough
for five years in jail. But if your partner confesses (called
'defection'), he will be set free and you get 20 years. If you both
confess, you both get 10 years.

Game theory assumes that you want the best outcome
for yourself. The possible outcomes for each strategy can be
assigned number-pairs, and analysed mathematically. The
answer turns out to be that you should confess. Yes, you both
get 10 years, then, but that it is better than taking the risk that
your partner will confess and land you with 20 years. This is
the least worst-case scenario, the minimax.

This seemed such a beautifully simple way of devising
strategy that the American military adopted it wholeheartedly
and it underpinned the nuclear arms race as generals assumed
the Russians were playing the same game and racing to build up
a nuclear arsenal. Von Neumann himself urged a pre-emptive
nuclear strike on Moscow to halt the buildup. Fortunately for
the world, everyone held back.

Later, game theory came to play a key role in economics
and even evolutionary theory. But while the mathematics is
elegantly simple, and the theory can often throw new light on
many situations, it is a far-from-perfect model of human, and
animal behaviour, and it remains controversial.

1931

ASSOCIATED MATHEMATICIAN:

Kurt Gödel

CONCLUSION:

An ancient Greek paradox was used to challenge the objective truth of mathematics.

IS IT COMPLETE?

CHALLENGING THE HEART OF MATHEMATICS

One is one and two plus two is four. That's a self-evident truth, isn't it? Well, that's what most thinkers long believed. While other concepts could ultimately be a matter of opinion, mathematics was always held to be the undiluted truth. If you could prove a mathematical theory, you had found the truth.

The whole logical structure of mathematics

About a century ago, however, some mathematicians and philosophers wanted to put this on a firmer footing. They were prompted by recent developments in set theory, which had begun to organize maths in terms of sets. Just as 2,300 years ago, Euclid had set out a number of basic starting points or axioms to build the whole edifice, so some mathematicians wanted to do this for the whole of mathematics. The enterprise began between 1910 and 1913 with Bertrand Russell and Alfred Whitehead's monumental *Principia Mathematica* (deliberately echoing the title of Newton's great book of 1687). Their aim was to examine the whole internal logical structure of mathematics and ultimately reduce it to basic principles on which everything else could be logically built.

It was a huge task. Naturally enough, Russell and Whitehead devoted a huge chunk of one of the three giant volumes just to pinning it down. But overall the progress seemed substantial enough for the great German mathematician David Hilbert to embark on a programme to build a complete set of axioms from which all mathematics could be built. Such a system of axioms would be consistent and complete, so that all proofs stemming from these axioms must by definition be true. If it is logically consistent, you cannot come up with two contradictory answers. If it is complete, every statement has a proof.

By the early 1930s, Hilbert's work was substantially finished and just needed a few small gaps filling in, identified as 23 problems. That's when a young Austrian mathematician named Kurt Gödel made a crucial, and ultimately devastating intervention. In 1931, Gödel wrote a paper entitled 'On Formally Undecidable Propositions in *Principia Mathematica* and Kelsey Systems', in which he laid out his two 'incompleteness' theorems.

The liar paradox

Gödel worked with an updated version of the old liar paradox, in which you ask whether you can believe someone when they say they never tell the truth. The story goes that the semi-mythical Cretan Epimenides asserted 'All Cretans are liars.' So was he telling the truth or not? This is not quite the liar paradox, since he could have simply been lying, and knew at least one Cretan who told the truth. So some logicians pinned it down to the sentence: 'This statement is false.' If the statement is indeed false, then it paradoxically must be true, and vice versa.

What Gödel did was explore this statement, or rather the statement, 'This statement has no proof' as it applied to maths. Proofs in maths are essentially saying that one set of numbers equals another, and numbers are just symbols. So Gödel could have made an arithmetical equivalent of the statement 'This theorem has no proof' either as an arithmetic procedure or as an algorithm in a series of prime numbers cubed.

His approach was to turn the statement into an arithmetic proposition, saying, effectively, 'This theorem has no proof.' And at once there is a problem. Either it has a proof or it

doesn't. If it has a proof, the theorem is self-contradictory. If it has no proof, it runs right up against the basic premise of completeness in Hilbert's programme: 'Every statement has a proof.'

In the other part of his two theorems, Gödel showed that exactly the same twist applies to consistency. He showed that if arithmetic is consistent, there can be no proof of its consistency. And if someone finds a proof of arithmetic's consistency, it will show that it's not consistent.

Gödel's hammer blow

So in a single paper, Gödel had demolished the central tenets of Hilbert's axioms, consistency and completeness. It was a hammer blow, not just for Hilbert's programme but mathematics in general. For a while, some hoped it was just a technical glitch, but further work by other mathematicians showed that the argument works for all axiomatic systems.

It meant that mathematics could no longer be seen as an arbiter of truth, and it could no longer be said that a mathematical proof is a statement of truth. Similarly, a statement may be true, but it may not be provable. This possibility had not occurred to mathematicians in over two thousand years since the time of the ancient Greeks. Mathematical logic was a simple yes or no. A theorem was either true or false, provable or disprovable. It meant there had to be third way: yes, no, or don't know for sure.

In theory, it meant the edifice of maths was a house of cards. In practice, it actually made little difference except to those like Hilbert who were trying to build it. The one exception was the growing field of computer science where binary answers and certainty were crucial, and here it provoked a crisis that took some time to resolve.

WHAT IS A FEEDBACK LOOP?

1948

ASSOCIATED
MATHEMATICIAN:
Norbert Wiener

CONTROL AND COMMUNICATION THEORY

CONCLUSION:
Wiener's work with control systems inspired him to provide a mathematical formalization of the idea of feedback.

American mathematician Norbert Wiener became fascinated by the idea of control systems during World War II. He was working with anti-aircraft guns and wanted to find a way for the guns automatically to target and shoot down enemy aircraft. And as he worked he began to think about control systems and how they rely on feedback.

Feedback was hardly a new idea. All living things rely on feedback to help them adjust and respond to their surroundings. Humans, like all creatures, rely on a continual supply of data from our senses to guide us through even the simplest tasks. And machines that respond to changes automatically are as old as civilization – like millponds, which automatically overspill when they become too full.

But it was Wiener in his 1948 book *Cybernetics: Or Control and Communication in the Animal and the Machine* who first analysed feedback mechanisms, both in the natural world and in machines in detail after the war. As he worked on his anti-aircraft gun, he had seen how this feedback often fails. If there were any delay in the feedback of data, for instance, the gun could misbehave, firing one side of the target then the other as it tried to stabilize.

Circular information

Wiener wondered if there were any similarities between these feedback failures and those in the human brain. He'd of course have been aware of the body's reflex loops: the way the nervous system short-circuits the brain, for instance, to jerk your hand out of the way if you touch a scorching-hot surface. But he wanted something more specific and asked a neurologist about a condition in which one of the control centres of the brain, the cerebellum, is damaged. The result is that a patient overshoots then undershoots when trying to reach for something, a disorder known as an intention tremor. When the brain does not get feedback from the hand fast enough to control the hand's position, it starts to flap back and forth. As he continued his research after the war, Wiener became aware of the circularity of feedback. There is a continual circular interplay between action and reaction, initiation and response, cause and effect. With feedback, any change stimulates a reaction that feeds back to the stimulant in what he called a feedback loop.

Positive and negative loops

Wiener realized that there is a major difference between positive feedback loops and negative feedback loops. A positive feedback loop is when the feedback amplifies the signal. You may have been to a live event where the microphone picks up the sound from the speakers and amplifies it in a horrible escalating squeal. Often, despite the positive name, positive feedback is the very opposite of control. It can be what you might call a vicious circle, when things start escalating – as when the warming of the world's climate melts permafrost, releasing methane, which warms the climate more.

It's negative feedback loops that normally provide control. This is when the system is stabilized because once the output reaches a certain intensity the response cuts the output. Whenever your central heating gets too hot, for instance, the thermostat automatically switches it off as the sensors respond to the rise in temperature.

Maxwell's governor

Negative feedback devices have a long history, but they weren't studied mathematically until James Clerk Maxwell's groundbreaking paper 'On Governors' in 1868. Governors were the simple and ingenious control mechanisms invented by James Watt in 1788 to control the speed of steam engines. As the engine speeds up, the shaft of the governor moves faster and centrifugal force pushes metal balls up. This pulls a lever that closes the engine throttle. So the engine slows down, the balls drop and the throttle opens again.

Maxwell's interest in the circularity of control emerged from the realization of the circulation of heat and energy in heat engines developed by Frenchman Sadi Carnot in the 1820s. And Maxwell's paper drew the idea of control loops into mainstream science. The title for Wiener's book, *Cybernetics*, acknowledges his debt to Maxwell, coined by Wiener from the Greek for 'governor'.

The cybernetic future

Wiener's book, though, takes the theory of control mechanisms using feedback much further. He identifies 'black boxes', systems in which the input and the output are known but none of the internal processing, and 'white boxes', simple systems whose internal workings are predefined.

Wiener's book unleashed a huge interest in control mechanisms and feedback loops, and the word 'cybernetics' has become part of the public consciousness. Automatic control for machines has long been part of our world, but Wiener's book preceded a massive development of feedback-control mechanisms connected in part with the coming of computers.

Wiener himself envisaged a world full of automatic control systems, and the picture he painted was far from comfortable. He imagined machines, controlled by feedback systems, which work with so little need for human intervention that many human workers become redundant and are thrown on the scrapheap of life. And his ideas come into play in robotics, too, with feedback loops providing the mechanism for robots to intervene and respond in the world.

Feedback-control systems are now deeply embedded in our way of life, from self-regulating kitchens to self-driving cars. But Wiener did not have a very positive view of these developments.

1948

ASSOCIATED
MATHEMATICIAN:

Claude Shannon

CONCLUSION:

Shannon solved the
problem of white noise
with binary maths.

WHAT IS THE BEST WAY TO TRANSMIT INFORMATION?

BINARY DIGITS AND DIGITAL SIGNALS

Transmitting any signal over a distance is beset with problems. There is the apocryphal story of a World War I general who sent the message: 'Send reinforcements; we are going to advance.' After various stages of transmission, the message finally received was 'Send three and fourpence; we are going to a dance.' In other words, as a signal is transmitted over a long distance, information is lost and the message is distorted.

Connection problems

In the 1940s, the telephone network was expanding and it seemed only natural to connect telephones under the Atlantic. After all, there had been a transatlantic telegraph for almost a century. But after the connection was made, it was found that when a message was sent through the Atlantic Ocean, it couldn't be read at the other end.

Telephone engineers looked for a technical solution to the issue. The problem was that as the signal crossed the Atlantic, it seemed to get weaker and weaker. So why not amplify the signal several times en route? The problem with that was that as a signal moves, it picks up errors: random background noise or 'white noise.' Amplifying the signal boosted the white noise as well. Eventually, this 'white noise' becomes so overwhelming that the message is lost.

It seemed an insurmountable obstacle, a fundamental feature of nature. But Claude Shannon, a mathematician and electronic engineer working at Bell Laboratories in the US, had other ideas, realizing the answer wasn't in a technical fix but in a new way of thinking about messages. In 1948, he published a paper entitled 'A Mathematical Theory of Communication'.

In this paper Shannon first identified just what information is. Information, he demonstrated, is basically something that is different. Background noise is random and effectively featureless. News is news because it hasn't been heard before. Information is unexpected. It is out of the ordinary. This is what makes it different from white noise.

This is not just true of telephone messages but all information. This insight has provided a whole range of insights into the way the world works, from the information that keeps living things living, to the information that shapes a drop of water.

Information entropy

In the nineteenth century, physicists such as Ludwig Boltzmann had tried to pin down the thermodynamic nature of order and disorder in the universe. In the second law of thermodynamics, they focused on the idea of entropy – maximum disorder – to which everything ultimately tends.

Shannon showed that information is order, and the loss of information in white noise is equivalent to disorder or entropy. He went on to develop an equation to show the probability of information being degraded. Shannon's equation is now the lynchpin of information theory.

Twenty years earlier, electronics engineer Ralph Hartley had introduced the idea of information as a measurable, mathematical quantity, and Shannon realized that the unexpectedness of information can be measured in a very simple way, and herein could be found the secret to noise-free transmission. The answer lay in binary maths.

0s and 1s

Binary maths is based on the idea that figures can be represented by just 0s and 1s. It dates back at least to the time of ancient Egypt. But it was rediscovered by Gottfried Leibniz

in 1679, then developed into a complete system of logic as Boolean algebra by George Boole in the mid nineteenth century.

Shannon realized that binaries could be used to define information's most basic units, its atoms. Every piece of information can ultimately be broken down into a yes/no, either/or, stop/go, on/off. In binary maths, this unit is 0 or 1. Every bit of information, Shannon realized, can be coded into strings of these basic chunks of 0s and 1s. He called them binary digits, 'bits', and the name has stuck.

Telephone messages then were transmitted by converting the vibrations created by speech into an electric current in which the voltage varies continually, mirroring the vibrations. This continually varying signal is now called 'analog'. And it is this analog signal that is so prone to white noise.

Shannon proposed that all the rich variety of speech can be reduced to a string of binary digits – that is, a digital code. The vibrations in the air that make speech are simply converted by an encoder into an electric signal in terms of 0s and 1s – every 0 a low voltage and every 1 a high voltage. This code of lows and highs is then used at the destination to recreate the speech.

Even this coded signal will suffer from white noise interference, but the difference between the 0s and 1s is so marked that it is much easier for the receiver to edit it out and reconstruct the original message. The signal can be cleaned up en route, too, using electronic devices to strip out background noise and send on only the digital message.

This system works so well that the vast majority of phone calls are transmitted digitally. But Shannon had not simply solved a technical problem; he had made a fundamental discovery about the nature of information. In showing that all information can be expressed as binary digits, Shannon provided an insight so powerful it launched the theory of information – with implications stretching into every field of science. And most dramatically of all, Shannon's paper opened the way to the digital technology that underpins all our computer and communications technology.

SHOULD YOU CHANGE YOUR STRATEGY?

NO-REGRETS GAME THEORY

1949

ASSOCIATED
MATHEMATICIAN:
John Nash

CONCLUSION:
Game theory is refined
by the idea of having 'no
regrets' with your decision.

In the late 1940s, as the world tried to recover from the terrors of World War II, American mathematicians began to develop a model of human behaviour that saw interactions as a game of strategy, in which every player is an individual out to get the best for themselves. The idea was called game theory, and the expectation was that, viewed this way, people's behaviour becomes, in theory, mathematically predictable.

John von Neumann, the Hungarian-born mathematician who first developed the idea with Oskar Morgenstern, believed that the way to play the game is to play not to win but to minimize your losses (see page 139). So the best strategy is the one which gives the least-bad worst-case scenario – a strategy that became known as 'minimax', the minimum possible maximum loss. But this strategy only really makes sense when you know absolutely nothing about your opponent. Essentially, it's saying, if you're in the dark, then it makes sense to play safe.

Game changer

But in most cases people do have some information, and if minimax was the only strategy in game theory, its applications might have been rather limited. But just a few years later in 1949, the brilliant mathematician John Nash added another key idea with a brief two-page paper. Nash's idea was literally a game changer.

Nash's idea is sometimes known as the theory of 'no regrets', because that's the aim: to have no regrets for your choice. It focuses on the idea that each of the players has a fair idea of how the other players will play the game, and have nothing to gain by changing strategy. So they reach a stand-off, in which no one gains or loses more than the others, now known as a Nash equilibrium.

The concept first emerged in the 1830s, when Antoine Cournot tried to pin down how manufacturers decide how much to produce compared to their rivals to maximize profits. If every firm boosts output, prices slump and profits drop, so Cournot concluded, firms adjust their output according to how much they believe their rivals will make. They reach a kind of equilibrium in output.

Battle of the sexes

Nash took this idea further and made it more widely applicable. One example is the Battle of the Sexes. It goes like this. Happy couple Bob and Alice want to go the cinema. They want to go together. But Alice wants to see an action movie and Bob wants to see a comedy. So what do they do? If they go their separate ways, neither gets any satisfaction or 'utility' as game theorists call it. But if they go together to either the action movie or the comedy, both get some utility, and one will actually enjoy it. Here the balance of utility between Bob and Alice in either choice is a Nash equilibrium.

Another famous example of how this works is 'The prisoner's dilemma' in which the players are two suspects arrested for a crime and put in separate cells (see page 140). If each protects the other by staying quiet then the police's scant evidence is only enough for five years in jail. But if one confesses, he will be set free and his fellow prisoner gets 20 years. If both confess, both get 10 years.

Neumann's minimax looked at it from just a single point of view, and concluded that you should confess to minimize the worst damage. Nash looked at it from both points of view, allowing each prisoner to guess what their partner might do; they may even discuss what to do in advance. Looked at this way, the outcome is the same as with minimax: that both prisoners should confess. But Nash's reasoning is different; this outcome occurs because neither will benefit from changing this strategy and keeping quiet. This is a balance of utility, or a Nash equilibrium.

The crucial thing is that if they subsequently find out what their fellow has done, neither prisoner will have any regrets about the choices they made. If one of them chooses to keep quiet and then finds the other has confessed, he of course ends up with a 20-year sentence and will bitterly rue the fact that he didn't own up.

War games

Nash's equilibrium concept ensured game theory was taken up widely in economics and also in psychology, evolutionary biology and a host of other fields. The way it seemed to provide a calculable understanding of strategic behaviour made it quickly a favourite with both economists and the military. Until recently, nearly all Nobel Prize-winners in economics incorporated it in their work, and it came to play a significant part in the US military strategy that drove the nuclear arms race in the 1950s and 1960s.

But some thinkers wonder how players actually reach an equilibrium in the first place, not knowing how other players will behave. Recently, mathematicians have shown a Nash equilibrium is hard to reach unless the players tell each other everything about their preferences. And with large numbers of players, it could take an almost infinite time to reach a balance.

Moreover, scientific experiments with the prisoner's dilemma show that people almost never adopt the Nash strategy, showing much more loyalty and solidarity than game theory assumes. Economists now broadly accept that people don't really behave as game theory predicts. And even Nash himself, who suffered from schizophrenia at the time he developed his ideas, came to doubt his work, saying when he was finally awarded the Nobel Prize himself in 1994: 'Gradually I began to intellectually reject some of the delusionally influenced lines of thinking which had been characteristic of my orientation.'

Nonetheless, many economists still consider Nash's 1948 paper to be one of the great breakthrough moments of the twentieth century.

CHAPTER 7: The Modern Computer Age: 1950 –

The maths behind them had been developing for a long time, but once the first computers were designed, their power evolved rapidly. The power computers offer mathematicians is boundless. Not only can they carry out complex sums and simulations in a fraction of the time it would take a human, but developments like the Internet allow mathematical collaboration to happen remotely and far quicker than ever before.

With calculations able to be carried out by a machine at the press of the button, it's not surprising that pure mathematics in particular has become more abstract and conceptual. Andrew Wiles's work on elliptic curves while solving Fermat's Last Theorem and Maryam Mirzakhani's work on topology are increasingly removed from the mathematics we see in the world around us. Yet they have provided us with some of the most stunningly beautiful results in all of mathematics.

1950

ASSOCIATED MATHEMATICIAN:

Alan Turing

CONCLUSION:

Turing's solution to a problem of mathematical logic was vital step on the road to modern computing.

CAN A MACHINE SOLVE ANY PROBLEM?

A SOLUTION TO THE DECISION PROBLEM

In 1936, while studying for his PhD at Princeton University, the young English mathematician Alan Turing published a short paper, 'On Computable Numbers, with an application to the *Entscheidungsproblem*'. It was a short paper, just 36-pages long, and purely about abstruse mathematical logic. Yet it was a turning point in history, marking the start of the modern computer age.

The *Entscheidungsproblem* or 'decision problem' was posed by David Hilbert and Wilhelm Ackermann in 1928. The challenge it threw out was to find an algorithm to decide whether a given statement is provable from the basic axioms using the rules of logic. The answer Turing came up with was a work of pure genius. He had no intention of creating the computer. He was just doing maths. Yet his insight laid out the maths that made computers possible.

Human computers

To solve the *Entscheidungsproblem*, Turing went right back to basics to work out just what was going on when mathematicians solved problems. What was the process? In Turing's day, 'computers' were simply people employed to calculate anything from tax bills to astronomical tables. But what they were actually doing? As he stripped it down to its basics Turing realized that nothing else was needed but a set of rules. The human mind is remarkable in its capacity for intelligence and ability to think. But when it comes to computing, all you need is a set of instructions. It could be reduced to a mechanical process not requiring thinking.

Really, there are only two aspects to calculation: an input of data, and a guide to what to do. So if the process is that mechanical, could you get a machine to do it? Yes, he answered. What you have to do, though, is give the machine the data and instructions in the right form.

Machine talk

With the same insight, he realized a machine cannot 'understand' anything but it can respond to instructions. These instructions have to be in the simplest possible form – stop/go, on/off. But using the 0s and 1s of binary logic, you can create a code that can tell the machine virtually anything.

So Turing envisaged a hypothetical mathematical machine that was controlled by instructions written in squares with a 0 or 1 on an incredibly long paper tape. As the tape scrolls through, the machine reads the code, and reacts accordingly. The machine moves the tape back and forth and, at any one time, reads a single symbol, or square, on the tape and responds accordingly. It may ignore the symbol, write on the square, move the tape one way or the other, or change to a new state. In this way, the machine could be fed step by step the detailed instructions, the algorithm it needed to solve the problem - which now, of course, we'd call a program.

Turing company

Turing had no idea of a real mechanical computer when he was devising this hypothetical machine. It was simply a way to answer to the *Entscheidungsproblem*, the decision problem, which boiled down to this: could there exist, at least in principle, a definite method or procedure by which all mathematical questions could be decided?

If, Turing reasoned, one could theoretically create a mechanical process that could actually do this, then the challenge would be answered. And the beauty of Turing's concept meant that all you have to do to get the machine to do something new is give it new instructions – a new section on the tape, or a new tape. And of course, it was theoretically

possible to create the instructions to do anything. This is why Turing's conceptual machine came to be called the Universal Turing Machine.

As Turing says right at the start of his remarkable paper,

Although the subject of this paper is ostensibly [just] the computable numbers. It is almost equally easy to define and investigate computable functions of an integral variable or a real or computable variable, computable predicates, and so forth.

In other words, throw a maths problem at it; it will solve it.

Up for anything

Clearly, complex tasks required very long instructions and complex programming. But the genius of the concept is that with the right program, the machine can do anything you want it to. It was a fundamental insight into the nature of information, implying that information alone is enough to direct the universe. And in time it also unleashed the computing revolution. Music players, phones, electronic keyboards, flight control systems and every electronic device conceivable are basically the same computing machine, just with different instructions and different output. Software, apps, programs are nothing more in essence than the long sequence of 0s and 1s on Turing's imaginary tape.

Using the ideas from his paper, Turing helped to build one of the first real mechanical computers to try and crack the Enigma Code used to encrypt all German military communication. The Enigma Code was considered unbreakable. But in 1941, Turing's computer helped break it, allowing the British to decipher countless secret messages. Some believe that this gave the Allies an advantage that enabled them to bring the war to an end two years earlier than they might otherwise have done, and so saved millions of lives. But it was the theoretical Turing Machine that really changed the world.

HOW DID A BUTTERFLY CAUSE A TORNADO?

THE MATHEMATICS OF THE UNPREDICTABLE

1963

ASSOCIATED
MATHEMATICIAN:
Edward Lorenz

CONCLUSION:
Lorenz showed that
in a complex system,
a small change can
have a negligible
or chaotic effect.

In 1972, meteorologist Edward Lorenz gave a talk at the 139th meeting of the American Association for the Advancement of Science entitled 'Does the flap of a butterfly's wings in Brazil set off a tornado in Texas?' The title was a simple provocative hook dreamed up by conference host Philip Merilees to sum up Lorenz's thesis that a small event can trigger huge changes. But the idea of the Butterfly Effect really caught on, and has cropped up in countless ways unimagined by Lorenz. It has, in a way, become a metaphor for itself: a small idea triggering a tsunami of fascination.

A misunderstood butterfly

The idea that a small difference can have a major effect is indeed beguiling. It seems suddenly to endow us each with powers so great they seem magical, even frightening. In Stephen King's story, '11/22/63', a young man named Jake finds a way to travel back into the past and prevent Lee Harvey Oswald from assassinating President Kennedy, believing this will be of huge benefit to mankind. But when Jake returns to the present, he finds the world in chaos, after a nuclear Armageddon has destroyed much of the world. Appalled, he returns to the past to let the assassination happen.

But this apparent superpower misses the point of Lorenz's insight. He was not saying that small effects have a big impact, and, like a lever, magnify their power. Instead, he was saying that in a complex system, small events can have a tiny effect or a massive one, and that it is impossible to work out which.

Predicting the weather

The idea came to Lorenz when he started running models on computers in the 1960s to try and make weather predictions. On one occasion, he rounded down a figure for the initial condition from 0.506127 to 0.506. It seemed a small, imperceptible change in a giant system. And yet the weather that resulted was hugely different.

Gradually, over the next decade, Lorenz began to refine his thesis that systems as complex as weather are so sensitive to their starting conditions that tiny differences can have a huge effect on the outcome – and there is almost no way of predicting which way things will go. Such an unpredictable system, he described as chaotic and so his idea has come to be called chaos theory. He put it rather more scientifically:

> *In view of the impossibility of measuring initial conditions precisely, and thereby distinguishing between a central trajectory and a nearby noncentral trajectory, all nonperiodic trajectories are effectively unstable from the point of view of practical prediction.*

This plain statement doesn't seem world-shaking, and yet it is just that. The universe is an infinitely complex place. But after Newton introduced his laws of motion, scientists assumed that it at least behaved in a deterministic way. There is a simple relationship between cause and effect, even if you can't always see it. One thing happens because another thing happens, in accordance with Newton's laws. Ultimately, then, the future of the universe is mechanically predetermined, right down to the movement of atoms; the events of the past inevitably determine the future.

Trying to pin down the universe

Scientists and mathematicians believed that if they could find the right laws, equations and data, then everything could be predicted with precision. In the eighteenth century, Pierre-Simon Laplace asserted that unpredictability has no place in the universe, saying that if we knew all the physical laws of nature, then 'nothing would be uncertain and the future, as the past, would be present to [our] eyes.'

Even the introduction of statistical approaches by Boltzmann and the uncertainties of quantum mechanics didn't entirely dispel this belief. But at the turn of the last century Henri Poincaré (see page 124) found himself defeated in his calculations of planetary orbits by the way small differences at the start had a huge effect on the outcome.

Poincaré concluded that scientists had been ignoring the huge influence of chance. He was not challenging the idea of the deterministic universe, but suggesting that differences so small they can be described as chance can have a major impact.

Lorenz went further. He, too, was not throwing out the idea of cause and effect, but saying that in some complex natural systems the effect of a little difference is so unpredictable that the idea of determinism becomes rather meaningless. It becomes impossible to trace a linear relationship between starting point and outcome, and the linear relationships envisioned in Newtonian mechanics simply don't work.

Forecasting

So there is no way that meteorologists would ever find a straightforward line that they could calculate to forecast the future, no matter how good their data or equations. However, Lorenz tried to get a good approximation of the most likely outcomes by using sets of slightly different starting conditions to conduct parallel meteorological simulations. These in turn developed into 'ensemble' weather forecasting methods, which use combinations of probabilities to achieve good predictions some way into the future.

Chaos theory has caught the public imagination with the idea that the universe is like a terrifying primordial mess. But for scientists it has proved rather more useful, indicating that they might better understand complex systems, from evolution to robotics, by looking not for linear relationships but for overall patterns.

1974

ASSOCIATED
MATHEMATICIANS:
Roger Penrose and
MC Escher

CONCLUSION:
Beautiful tessellations that
never repeat are proven
to be possible.

WHAT DO DARTS AND KITES COVER?

PENROSE'S MESMERIZING TILES

The buildings of Islam are often adorned with stunningly beautiful and intricate patterns of tiles. Mathematicians find patterns of tiles like this, called tessellations, especially fascinating because they throw up interesting mathematical conundrums. Indeed, some argue that Islamic tiling patterns are in effect algorithms.

But in the last half-century, mathematicians have become especially interested in how tessellations are organized and how patterns might fit together on a vast scale. It was the same kind of fascination mathematicians had with patterns of numbers, and they began to wonder if they could find regular tilings that never repeated, known as aperiodic tilings.

The problem with fivers

Periodic tilings always repeat the same pattern. The square tiles on your bathroom floor are periodic tilings. The pattern will always be the same no matter how far you go. Triangles fit together to form a periodic tiling pattern, too. As do hexagons. Mathematicians call this translational symmetry, which means that as you move across it, the pattern is always the same. But pentagons, five-sided figures, don't even form a tiling pattern. Try to fit pentagons together and you get gaps between them.

Johannes Kepler showed how the gaps between pentagons could be filled in with five-pointed stars or pentagrams in 1619, and when the brilliant Roger Penrose became interested in tessellations in the 1950s, he acknowledged Kepler's work as an inspiration. But Penrose wasn't just interested in pentagons; he was interested in symmetry breaking, and aperiodic tilings.

Artist of the impossible

The Dutch artist MC Escher, famous for his 'impossible' drawings, was interested in tessellations, too. In the 1950s, Escher had done two prints of aperiodic tiling, entitled *Mosaic 1* and *Mosaic 2*, using interlocking shapes of animals. But beyond the frame of the picture, the only way the pattern could continue was for the artist to invent ever more shapes.

By this time, Penrose and Escher already knew each other and had been corresponding on the subjects of tessellations. And in 1962, Penrose went to visit Escher in the Netherlands, and gave him a small wooden puzzle of identical geometric shapes. To Escher's astonishment, these tiles would only fit together in one way. It went against his belief that regular tilings repeated indefinitely.

Escher began to puzzle away at the idea of a non-repeating tessellation, and eventually in 1971 came up with a drawing made from interlocking shapes of ghosts. Uniquely among his drawings it was indeed aperiodic.

Five star performance

Meanwhile, Penrose, too, had been working at aperiodic patterns using shapes based on the pentagon. He came up with three different sets. The first one uses four shapes: a pentagon, a five-point star, a boat (3/5 of a star) and a thin diamond. The third uses rhomboids. But the second, which he unveiled in 1974, is the most remarkable and won Penrose lasting fame. This is made from just two four-sided shapes, a kite and a dart.

There are rules in Penrose tiling about how you fit the tiles together, and with the kite and dart there is a key rule that you cannot insert the kite into the V of the dart to form a rhomboid. There is something astonishing about the way these two simple shapes interact. Previously it had been assumed you'd need thousands of shapes to create an aperiodic tiling. But with the kite and dart, you could do it with two shapes. In 1984, Penrose was able to show they could spread over an infinite plane in an infinite number of arrangements, never once repeating.

Five-a-side

It had been assumed before that fivefold patterns just never occurred in nature. But once Penrose discovered five-based tiling, scientists began to discover real-world examples, too, not just on a plane but in three dimensions as well. In the standard models of crystal symmetry, for instance, fivefold symmetry was deemed impossible.

In 1982, chemist Dan Shechtman was analysing a crystal and discovered it did indeed have a fivefold structure. The result was so outrageous that for sometime Shechtman was ridiculed for making a mistake. Even Penrose was surprised. It was a real shocker, because if crystals did form in this way, the whole understanding of crystal structure would have to be revised. But it turned out he was right, and he had discovered a new kind of crystal, called a quasi-crystal.

Since then, many other quasi-crystals like this have been found, and then in 2011, Shechtman won the Nobel Prize for chemistry. Many felt Penrose deserved to be included in the prize, too, for without his extraordinary discovery, quasi-crystals might never have been identified.

In Helsinki, an entire street is laid out in Penrose kites and darts, and the effect is surprisingly pleasing to the eye.

Penrose tiling

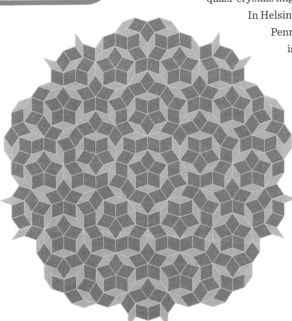

DID FERMAT HAVE A PROOF?

SOLVING FERMAT'S LAST THEOREM

1994

ASSOCIATED
MATHEMATICIAN:
Andrew Wiles

CONCLUSION:
A centuries-old maths
problem is solved by
cutting-edge techniques
in number theory.

Back in 1637, French mathematician Pierre de Fermat was studying *Arithmetica*, an ancient Greek text written about CE 250 by Diophantus (see page 46). *Arithmetica* was the classic text on number theory, Fermat's own speciality, and as he read, he often scrawled notes in the margin.

One page particularly intrigued Fermat. This was the page in which Diophantus drew attention to the equation made famous by Pythagoras about the squares on the side of a right-angle triangle. This was the equation $x^2 + y^2 = z^2$, best known in the form $3^2 + 4^2 = 5^2$. Diophantus invited his readers to come up with solutions to equations in this form.

For Fermat, this was clearly old hat, and his marginal notes began to explore similar equations with powers greater than a square, starting with cubes, $x^3 + y^3 = z^3$. Fermat jotted down that there was no solution to this equation. He then went on to state that, in fact, there was no solution to this form of equation with any power n, $x^n + y^n = z^n$, where n is greater than two. It was a staggering claim. But Fermat wrote, 'I have discovered a truly marvellous proof of this, which this margin is too small to contain.' And then wrote no more.

The never-ending treasure hunt

For mathematicians who came after, this marginal hint was unbelievably tantalizing. It was like saying you'd found where Blackbeard's treasure was, but failed to leave a map. Some even believed he was making it up, or at very best had discovered a flawed proof. There were other marginal ideas in Fermat's book, but they all gradually yielded to proof. But this one resisted all-comers, and so it became known as Fermat's Last Theorem. Proving (or disproving) Fermat's Last Theorem became the

Holy Grail for number theorists, and the pursuit, though vain, spurred many of the major advances in the field, even if only by getting mathematicians excited by the mystery.

In one particularly dramatic story, which may or may not be true, rich German industrialist and amateur mathematician Paul Wolfskehl, was on the point of suicide, some say because of a girl. He decided to shoot himself in the head at midnight. But before he did, he went to the library and began to read a paper by Ernst Kummer on Fermat's Last Theorem. Spotting a flaw, he at once began to work on his own solution so avidly that he missed his date with death. Whatever the truth, when he died in 1906, he bequeathed 100,000 marks to the first person to prove Fermat's Last Theorem.

A little boy's quest

But despite the added lure of the prize, no one had solved the mystery when, in 1963, a 10-year-old boy with a passion for maths named Andrew Wiles borrowed a book about it by mathematician Eric Temple Bell from his local library in Cambridge. Bell predicted gloomily that humanity would be destroyed by nuclear war before anyone solved Fermat's Last Theorem. Of course, young Andrew was at once determined to prove him wrong.

It took Wiles around 30 years to do it but eventually, in 1994, to the world's astonishment, he succeeded. Wiles's proof emerged from a conjecture made just a few years earlier by Japanese mathematicians Yutaka Taniyama and Goro Shimura. Their idea linked elliptical curves, which involve cubic equations, with modular forms (functions rather like sines and cosines). No one could prove the conjecture but most mathematicians were convinced enough by it for it to inspire other work.

A curved ball hits the spot

In 1986, by which time Wiles was a professor at Princeton, fellow Princeton professor Ken Ribet, building on work by German mathematician Gerhard Frey, made a remarkable link between the Taniyama-Shimura conjecture and Fermat's

Last Theorem. Ribet constructed an elliptical curve based on a hypothetical 'solution' to the Fermat equation that would contradict Taniyama-Shimura. If this proved correct, then Fermat (and Taniyama-Shimura) was wrong. But if someone could prove Taniyama-Shimura, then that would pretty much prove Fermat.

Wiles, who had all but abandoned his quest for a solution, was energized. He'd also been working on elliptical curves, and now he saw a route to his goal. He worked in secret, confiding only in his wife. His method was to focus on a particular subset of elliptical curves. If he could prove they were modular in an infinite number of cases, he would demonstrate the Taniyama-Shimura link to Fermat and find the ultimate proof.

Even proving this small case required Wiles to come up with some ingenious new methods of working. But after seven years, he at last made his breakthrough and decided to go public at a conference in his hometown, Cambridge, on 23 June 1993. The conference listened enthralled as he unfolded his thesis. He wrapped up with the bombshell: 'Which proves Fermat's Last Theorem.' He smiled then added, 'I think I'll leave it there.'

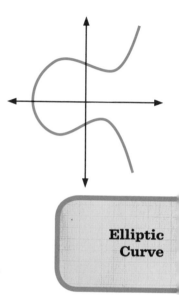

Elliptic Curve

Correcting the flaw

The media went wild, but then as Wiles checked his huge and complicated proof, ready to send it to authenticators as usual, he discovered a flaw. To prove that the argument was true for an infinite number of cases, he only had to prove that one proven case inevitably led to the next, like a domino effect. The problem was, it didn't. Wiles was devastated. Not only had he not beaten the Fermat demon after all, but he had announced to the world that he had.

Confiding only in his former student Richard Taylor, Wiles went back to work to fix the error. Suddenly on 19 September 1994, he had a brainwave. What if the error was not a flaw, but the route to the proof? It quickly proved to be so, and Wiles was finally able to send off his work, which was verified by his peers over the next three years. Finally, on 27 June 1997, Wiles collected the Wolfskehl Prize.

2014

**ASSOCIATED
MATHEMATICIAN:**
Maryam Mirzakhani

HOW DO THINGS
CURVE?

CONCLUSION:
Mirzakhani's award-winning work provided groundbreaking insight into the workings of curved surfaces.

THE DYNAMICS OF RIEMANN SURFACES

The late Maryam Mirzakhani was not only the first woman to win the coveted Fields Medal, in 2014, the maths equivalent of the Nobel Prize; she was also the first Iranian to win. The news of her death in 2017 shocked and saddened the maths community, and tributes to her genius poured in from across the world.

Mirzakhani's area of interest was entirely hypothetical, high-level maths: maths that has no apparent practical value but is an intellectual challenge of the highest order. This is maths that stretches the imagination to its limits and may indeed offer real world insights, in time.

Curved surfaces

What stirred Mirzakhani's interest was the geometry and complexities of abstract curved surfaces. These surfaces can be created on a computer to look like real and familiar shapes such as spheres, saddle-shapes and doughnut shapes. But they can also be much more complex, twisting this way and that in space. As they turn around and rotate they reveal different aspects of their shapes. When created on screen they are often done in shimmering rainbow colours, with a grid of squares across them. Both the colours and the squares indicate what they are – graphs of complex mathematical functions. The squares work like the coordinates on a conventional graph, but the changing colours, too, indicate changing functions.

Riemann's projections

The idea for these surfaces was introduced by German mathematician Bernhard Riemann in the nineteenth century to help handle complex problems in analysis in a geometric way, and so they are called Riemann surfaces. Riemann didn't have the benefit of colourful computer animations, but conceptually they are the same. What these imaginary surfaces do is map complex and imaginary numbers and functions at the same time as real numbers.

In some ways, they are more like map projections in reverse, and some of the basic geometric ideas were first developed by Gerardus Mercator in the sixteenth century as he tried to work out a way of 'projecting' the spherical surface of the Earth accurately onto a flat map for the first time. Key to Mercator's projection was changing the lines of latitude and longitude on the globe, which are both entirely curved and, in the case of longitude, converge at the poles, into a grid of squares on a flat map. Riemann surfaces are rather like map projections in reverse, projecting the values from a complex plane onto curves.

Riemann created the surfaces named after him to develop ideas by Gauss about geodesics – the shortest distance between two points on a curved surface – and curvature (how much a surface bends compared to the flat plane of Euclidean geometry). Riemann wanted to create multidimensional spaces where many variables can be mapped simultaneously. The more variables there are, the more dimensions. In this way, Riemann laid the foundations of modern differential geometry with the idea of a multidimensional manifold (surface) and the idea of distance defined in metrics (graphic measures).

Riemann surface for the function $f(z) = \sqrt{z}$

Painting maths

What Mirzakhani did was take these mathematical surfaces and explore and play with them in dizzying new ways. Her great ability was to take complex mathematical problems and conjure up a new and highly imaginative solution using Riemann surfaces and moduli. Mirzakhani would sit on the floor sketching out ideas on giant sheets of paper, leading her infant daughter Anahita to exclaim, 'Oh, Mommy is painting again!'

In this way Mirzakhani created new techniques for finding geodesics and studied the dynamics of how particles flow over different curved surfaces – imagine a billiard ball running down a bobsleigh run or a saddle or a ball or a doughnut (the ring-shaped kind that mathematicians call a torus). And she made studies of how a billiard ball might bounce around on a polygonal table, which could give important insights into the movement of gases.

Geodesics on hyperbolic surfaces

One of Mirzakhani's great achievements was her study of geodesics on a hyperbolic (saddle-shaped) surface. It was already known that as the surface grows longer, the total possible number of geodesics grows exponentially. But Mirzakhani found that if she excluded geodesics that intersect, the total number grows instead as a polynomial. This enabled her to develop clear formulae for complex calculations involving polynomial coefficients. Brilliant American physicist Edward Witten used Mirzakhani's formulae to make a crucial new contribution to the heady physics of string theory, which Witten had pioneered.

Mirzakhani's work has already had a big impact on mathematics, and may lead to new developments in engineering, cryptography and theoretical physics, including studies of the origin of the universe.

WHAT IS A SCUTOID?

DISCOVERING A NEW SHAPE

2018

ASSOCIATED
MATHEMATICIANS:

Pedro Gómez-Gálvez et al

CONCLUSION:
Researchers studying
epithelial cells realized
they were a shape that
had never been
observed before.

In 2018, headlines announced, 'Scientists find new shape!' It intrigued everybody. The story originated in an article in *Nature Communications* and the scientists in the news were a team of mathematicians and biologists led by Pedro Gómez-Gálvez.

It turns out that the biologists were working on the structure of epithelial cells: the cells that form in layers to make skin and the lining of the guts. As they examined them closely, they realized the shapes weren't quite what they expected. Biologists had assumed that these cells were prisms – that is, regular six-sided columns (like a pencil cut to a stump). Such shapes would pack together neatly as the cells grew, forming a strong, watertight layer.

Of course, the layer has to bend round into all kinds of shapes, to turn corners and bend round bones. But biologists had assumed that all that happened was that the prisms narrowed at one end to allow the cells to pack tighter on one side than the other, like the bricks in a Roman arch. This pinched, rather cone-shaped prism is called a *frustum*. It was only natural to expect this shape. After all, this is how honeycombs are arranged.

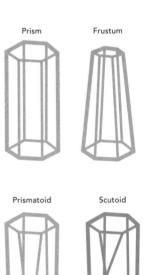

Prism   Frustum

Prismatoid   Scutoid

Odd faces

But the biologists noticed as the epithelial cells in fruit-fly embryos grew, at times one end of the cells contracted at certain corners, allowing them to make contact with their neighbours in different way. They couldn't quite understand how prisms could do this, and so they called in the team of mathematicians. Mathematicians are known for their interest in 3D tiling patterns, so surely they could come up with an answer? In fact, the task was much harder than the mathematicians expected. No shape that they were familiar with seemed to fit the bill. They developed computer models and realized that frustra would work only if the surface curved in the same way in all directions. But as the epithelial cells grow, they bend and twist and fold into all kinds of shapes, and the inner and outer ends of the cells contact different, not the same, neighbours as would be inevitable with prisms. Cells pack together along faces and edges, but they need energy to build and maintain these borders, and the larger contact the cells have, the more energy they have to spend. So they need faces as small as possible.

The y-shaped side

Eventually the modellers realized that the best solution is if one of the sides of the shape splits into a triangle at the top, so that the corner of the cell is not a single vertical line but a y-shape. These are not easy shapes to imagine. But if you think of the pencil stump, then diagonally slice off one corner and you've got something like it.

The beautiful thing about this shape is not just that it has different numbers of corners at each end, but that the triangular slice allows cells to pack together in many different kinds of orientation. This shape is great for packing and minimizing energy use.

To the mathematicians, who had never seen this shape before, it was an exciting discovery. If this is indeed how nature packs cells together, it must surely be an important shape, and the way it packs together must mean that there are some exciting mathematical properties waiting to be discovered. After all, there must be a reason cells all develop in this shape.

The beetle box

The scientists decided to name their new shape a 'scutoid', principally because of its resemblance to a beetle, though some say it's a nod to one of the team, Luis M. Escudero. But having made their perfect mathematical shape and given it a name, they needed to know if it was just a theory.

And so they went looking for their scutoids in nature, and they found them in abundance. As they peered through their microscopes, they suddenly saw this shape they must have seen countless times before and simply failed to recognize. The could see them as individual epithelial cells divided, aggregated, curved and folded to form salivary glands and egg chambers.

Hunting for scutoids

The scutoid hunt has barely begun but everyone expects many more examples to be found. It may be that we ourselves are made of scutoids. And perhaps some honeycombs, which seem to be hexagonal, are in fact made of scutoids. Of course, the scutoids in nature are not as geometrically neat and regular as those in the modellers' computer creations. They are squished and stretched, bent and twisted – and of course each and every one is changing all the time. But there is little doubt that they are real and important shapes.

There are ideas that they could help in growing artificial organs and tissues in laboratories. Three-dimensional-printed scutoids might create a kind of scaffolding on which living epithelial cells can grow and self-organize, helping them grow quicker in the right shape. And who knows what discoveries mathematicians might make as they begin to explore the mathematics of this new shape? Yes, it is a shape that looks quite familiar, but if it is as common in nature as it seems to be, then it surely has much to teach us.

Glossary

Algorithm – A series of steps that, when followed, provides a solution to a problem

Axiom – An initial statement taken to be true without proof from which further results can be derived

Base – A number that is used as a basis for a number system and is thus the number of digits used in that system

Binary – A number system in base-2 which uses 0s and 1s

Calculus – The branch of mathematics that measures change

Coefficients – In algebra, a constant or number that a variable is multiplied by in an algebraic expression, appearing immediately before it, e.g. the 4 in 4x

Conjecture – A mathematical proposition based on incomplete information which has not been proven or disproven

Fractals – A shape that displays the same pattern as the whole when magnified

Fluid dynamics – The study of how liquids and gases behave and flow

Imaginary number – A number that is expressed as a quantity of i, the square root of -1

Infinitesimals – The smallest value possible that is more than nothing

Integer – A whole number

Irrational number – A real number that cannot be expressed as a ratio of two integers

Logarithm – The number that shows how many times a number has to be multiplied by itself to produce another given number

Logic – Using algebra and algebraic rules to express a proposition and assist in the process of reasoning

Number Theory – The branch of mathematics that deals with the study of integers

Place value – The system whereby the value a digit denotes depends on its position in a number

Polygon – A shape with at least three sides

Prime number – A number that can only be divided by one and itself

Proof – The process of showing that a mathematical statement is true, resulting in a theorem

Quadratic – An equation in which two is the highest power

Sexagesimal – A number system that uses 60 as its base

Statistics – The branch of mathematics concerned with organising and interpreting data

Theorem – A proposition that has been proved

Theory – A set of principles, statements and theorems that explain and constitute a branch of mathematics

Topology – The branch of mathematics that studies the geometric properties that are preserved when shapes are de-formed

Index